Presented to

Madison Ave. Baptist

In Memory of

Mrs. Martha Meinert

By

Evelyn&Emma Meyers

the
CROSS
and the
SCALPEL

the
CROSS
and the
SCALPEL

JAMES C. HEFLEY

WORD BOOKS,
Publisher
Waco, Texas

Dedicated
to my mother
who once wanted me to
become a doctor

Contents

The Healing Legacy — 240 Years

Swelling feet. Breathless on exertion. Coughing up mucoid sputum. Blood pressure 170/30. An enlarged heart, Patient Ranganathan's x-ray showed. *A damaged, leaky aortic valve,* further study indicated. If something drastic wasn't done soon, the poor rickshaw puller would go into heart failure.

Patient Ranganathan was fortunate. For nine months doctors at the Christian Medical College and Hospital in Vellore, India, had been working in their lab on a unique transplantation project, and they were making excellent progress. Two months after the stricken man entered the hospital, they removed his defective aortic valve and successfully inserted a calf's valve in its place.

This was the first such operation in Southeast Asia, and it was done in a missionary hospital.

Medical missions have indeed come a long way since the days when church leaders fought the advance of medicine. During the early sixteenth century, Roman Catholic administrators of the medical school–hospital at Bologna, Italy, actually forbade doctors to treat nonbelievers for longer than three days. And they discouraged the doctors from doing surgery on believers.

Not until 1730, and after the Reformation, was the first medical missionary sent out on the field. Under joint Danish and German sponsorship, Kaspar Gottlieb Schlegemilch went to India, but he died in Madras just one month after his arrival in the country.

Sixty-three years later, Dr. John Thomas became the second missionary doctor when he joined William Carey in India. Dr. Thomas fought vigorously against two native practices: the abandonment of sick babies, who were thought to be bewitched, to death by exposure, and the burning of Hindu widows upon the funeral pyres of their dead husbands. After eleven years, Carey's colleague went insane and had to be hauled away to the asylum in Calcutta.

The first American medical missionary was both minister and physician. A leaflet on "The Claims of 600 Million" had such a profound effect on Dr. John Scudder that he took his wife and young son to Ceylon the same year that he read it. Despite that son's death and the death of two more children during the next eighteen months, the Scudders trusted the Great Physician and moved to India where they continued healing and preaching.

Seven of nine surviving Scudder children became missionaries to India. Among four generations of Scudders, forty-two members of the family have given over eleven hundred combined years to missionary service. One of the forty-two, Dr. Ida S. Scudder, granddaughter of Dr. John, started the now famous Vellore Christian Medical College and Hospital in 1900. Vellore is now operated under inter-church auspices. One of the world's greatest international medical centers, it has a staff of 262 full-time doctors and 292 graduate students. It was the first in India to initiate recognized residency training in chest, brain, and heart surgery, and the first in the world to develop reconstructive surgery for leprosy patients.

The early medical missionaries were supporters of the "first team." They were sent to keep the missionaries, preachers, and teachers healthy. But as important new medical milestones were crossed in Europe and the United States (vaccination for smallpox, 1796; use of drugs for surgical anesthesia, 1846; recognition that fever was not a disease, but a symptom of disease; discovery that germs can cause infectious disease, 1877; and other developments), more and more pioneers began using medicine to "open doors for the gospel" and to follow Jesus' command to "heal the sick."

Dr. Peter Parker, the first American missionary to China, sailed in 1834. In addition to starting a modern teaching hospital, he helped pave the way for commercial and diplomatic relations. Only a year after Dr. Parker arrived in China, Dr. Asahel Grant began healing Muslims in Turkey in Christ's name. The next year Dr. Dan Beach Bradley began inoculating for smallpox in Thailand at a time when preventive medicine was practically unknown in Asia.

But despite difficulties in raising support at home and despite many personal tragedies (the first Southern Baptist physician to go to China, Dr. J. S. James, drowned in 1848 as his ship was preparing to dock), medical missions marched on.

In 1840, England's Dr. David Livingstone set out for Africa "with a burning desire to open the way for the gospel into regions where it had not been heard." The "explorer of the century," Dr. Livingstone, in the words of Florence Nightingale, "struck the first blow to abolish the hideous slave trade" and opened up the heart of black Africa to commerce and Christianity. His own heart was buried by grieving Africans on the eastern shore of Lake Tanganyika.

The first woman missionary doctor from the United States, Dr. Clara Swain, arrived in Bareilly, India, in 1870. She trained a class of fourteen from the girls' orphanage there to be nurses, and she carried on a large practice among the women and children of the area.

The first missionary nurse, Miss E. M. McKechnie, began work in Shanghai in 1884 and established a hospital there.

This same year, the first two Protestant medical missionaries arrived in Korea. They were forbidden to make converts until one, Dr. Horace Allen, saved the life of a prince. Dr. Allen subsequently became the first American ambassador to that country.

Shortly afterward, a friend of Dr. Oliver Avison of Toronto called him a fool for wanting to go to Korea and "bury" himself. "What can you do with all those millions of people?" he asked. Dr. Avison answered that he might train young Koreans to be good doctors and send them out to work for their own people. "Won't that be something?" he demanded of his critical friend.

About 1900, Dr. Avison founded Severance Union Medical College, today one of Asia's outstanding institutions of learning. Nearly two thousand doctors have graduated from Severance (now Yonsei). Since World War II, half of Korea's ministers of health have been alumni, as have several national university presidents as well.

Back in India, Englishwoman Dr. Edith Brown laid the foundation for Ludhiana Christian Medical College, the first Asian women's medical school. And across the world in Puerto Rico,

Dr. Grace Atkins in 1904 started the haven of mercy which has grown to be the world famous Presbyterian Hospital of San Juan.

These and other medical missionaries of the nineteenth and twentieth centuries are little known in the Western world, where we take medicine for granted. But many are national heroes in their respective countries of service. They are blessed many times over by the sufferers who benefit from their healing hands of mercy.

For example, a Sikh repairman who had worked at a Presbyterian hospital in India once said to a missionary, "Miss Sahib, when a place is as blessed as this hospital has been blessed over the years, it means that a great guru (teacher) has at some time found rest here. Did your Christ ever stop here?"

And at the Miraj Medical School in India (founded in 1897 by Dr. W. J. Wanless, the "Dr. Mayo" of India), a poor woman was delivered of her tenth child. The woman had no clothing for the baby so the missionaries dressed the infant in clothes sent by a women's organization. With tears of joy rolling down her cheek, the mother exclaimed, "Your God has made my only baby boy a king."

Now, almost a quarter of a millennium since the first medical missionary sailed to India, Protestant, Anglican, and Orthodox churches are currently spending over $100 million annually to support a vast complex of lighthouses of mercy. Presently, these churches give their support in 81 countries to 1239 hospitals, 4 medical schools at the M.D. level, 9 institutions for the training of medical assistants, and 412 professional schools of nursing, plus hundreds of small dispensaries and clinics.

The medical missionaries who serve from Nepal to Nigeria and from Yemen to New Guinea defy stereotyping. In addition to a smattering of dentists, there are over a thousand doctors, still more nurses, and growing numbers of medical technicians, hospital administrators, business managers, and even a few veterinarians.

They serve with boards of both large and small denominations and boards who accept missionaries from many evangelical backgrounds. Not a few of those who consider themselves under the banner of the cross work for private and government hospitals abroad or receive their support from some other nonsectarian source.

Fourteen dedicated individuals are profiled in the following chapters. The challenges, thrills, rewards, and, yes, the problems of medical missions in the seventies can better be seen by looking at real people in action than by surveying statistics.

2.

Sawbones of Ometepec

JAMES BOYCE, M.D.

Mix cattle rustlers, feuds, Indians, a frontier hospital, and a redheaded, sawed-off, mustached doctor, and you have, not the scenario for a Hollywood western film, but the real-life saga of missionary medic Dr. Jim Boyce.

A Canadian missionary introduced me to Dr. Jim in Mexico City. "Jim's from the wild state of Guerrero," he said. "More tourists and cattle rustlers in his state than any other in Mexico."

I looked down at the 5'6" doctor and pumped his hand. "I read about a little incident in Guerrero two or three days ago," I recalled. "Weren't twelve men killed in a feud before the Army moved in?"

The little doctor nodded but didn't smile. "That doesn't include the wounded, some of whom we treated."

Suddenly I noticed a jar of what appeared to be bullets in his left hand. He sensed my curiosity.

"They're real bullets. I'm going to use them as a talking point when I go home on furlough. Every one has a story behind it."

He unscrewed the lid and held up a misshapen bit of lead. "Two fellows had a little disagreement. One drew his gun and shot the other through the abdomen at close range. The bullet went through and lodged in the leg of a sixteen-year-old Amuzgo Indian boy standing behind him. The boy came to us. We x-rayed his leg, then dug this out of the bone it had splintered."

The tall Canadian nudged me. "Jim Boyce has a good story. Don't miss it."

I didn't.

Dr. Jim, I learned, manages the small 25-bed *Amistad* (Friendship) Hospital in the western frontier town of Ometepec, Mexico, southeast of swinging Acapulco. Here he welcomes mestizos, Indians, and, from nearby Pacific coastal villages, Negroes whose ancestors escaped from African slave ships.

His grandfather was a pioneer missionary for the Associated Reformed Presbyterian Church in the central state of San Luis Potosí. Jim never met him, but heard plenty about him when growing up in the Carolinas and Florida.

Young Jim allowed he would like to be a pioneer like his grandfather, if not in Mexico, perhaps in the mysterious Congo.

The Boyce family then lived in the middle of an orange grove in Florida, having moved from North Carolina when Jim was five. The Boyce family (two brothers and three sisters with Jim next to the youngest) attended the nearby Presbyterian church regularly where Jim thrilled to stories told by visiting missionaries.

By the time he was attending Erskine College in South Carolina, where his best grades were in chemistry, he was thinking of missionary medicine. But he kept dismissing the dream because he knew his widowed mother could not afford to send him to medical school. As it was, his older sister, Carolyn, a school teacher, was helping him on college expenses.

Still bent on a missionary career, however, Jim enrolled in Columbia Theological Seminary under a work scholarship. While in seminary he participated in the pastoral internship program. Just before he left for assignment as assistant pastor of a Presbyterian church in Birmingham, Alabama, the seminary president cautioned him: "Be careful about courting in the congregation. You'll cause too many problems."

But upon meeting a dark-haired, brown-eyed Southern belle named Marguerite Payne, he quickly forgot the president's admonition. They were married in May 1940, right after Jim finished seminary, and they crossed the border into Mexico as missionaries for the Southern Presbyterian church, all in the same month.

In Mexico City they began studying Spanish at the National University of Mexico. There they met Dr. Hervey Ross, a Presbyterian missionary doctor studying in the University's medical school. The meeting was a turning point in Jim's future. Dr. Ross explained that although he was qualified to practice in the

United States, he had to complete five years of training in
Mexico in order to practice there. "Tuition is cheap," he told
Jim. "Why don't you get your medical training here in Mexico
City and then intern in the States?"

Jim consulted the Presbyterian Board and they granted permission. The five years turned out to be invaluable. He earned
his Mexican M.D., became proficient in Spanish, got to know
scores of future Mexican doctors, and gained an intimate understanding of Mexican scholarship. Then he went shopping for a
place of service.

"I can tell you where a hospital is most needed," a government
health official told him, "but you probably wouldn't want to go
there. It's quite primitive."

"We want to go where the need is greatest," Jim said. The
official ran his finger down the map along the western coastline.
"Here about 125 miles south of Acapulco and 30 miles inland is
Ometepec. Population is about ten thousand. Two or three doctors there, but they've never had a hospital. And the town
doctors don't get out to the rural people."

Dr. Jim hitched a ride to Ometepec in an old Boeing cargo
plane carrying ice and vaccine for a program to eradicate hoof-
and-mouth disease among cattle. While the vets vaccinated, he
looked around the dusty town. Nestled in a forested valley with
hot sulphur springs close by, it reminded him of what the western United States may have been like about 1850. Colorful
Amuzgo Indians, swashbuckling Mexicans in broad-brimmed
hats and wearing sidearms, and horses clopping along the cob-
blestoned main street created a picturesque scene. He learned
there was no evangelical church in the town, although two
teams of Wycliffe Bible translators had recently moved into an
Amuzgo Indian village a day's trail hike up into the mountains.

He returned to Mexico City for Marguerite and their four
young children. When the Boyces told town leaders that the
Presbyterian church would like to establish a hospital where
everyone would be welcome, the leaders were excited at the
prospect. They wanted the hospital but weren't sure if the
Boyces as evangelicals would be appreciated. "There might be
trouble from some narrow-minded fanatics," a friendly Catholic
priest warned Dr. Jim. "But I hope you'll come anyhow!"

"We're going back to the States for a year," Dr. Jim told the
priest and other leaders. "I want to do my internship and raise
funds for some equipment. We'll be back."

While he interned at the Medical College Hospital of the University of Virginia, he somehow also found time to learn to fly at Le Tourneau Flight School in Georgia. Upon completing flight training, Dr. Jim gave lessons to another new missionary appointee, Johnny Wood, who also planned to serve in Mexico.

The "liberal" Catholic priest and other town leaders welcomed Dr. Jim and Marguerite back to Ometepec. But the Boyces had trouble renting a house because they were evangelicals. Finally, after several days of inquiring, they secured two adobe residences across the street from each other. One served as living quarters and the other as a clinic.

Just two weeks after the Boyces arrived, Johnny and Madge Wood flew into Ometepec in a small Cessna 180. Remarkably enough, the two couples found they had just the right voices to form a quartet: Johnny sang bass, Madge soprano, Marguerite alto, and Dr. Jim tenor. Sunday evenings they gathered around the piano and harmonized on hymns. Attracted by the music, neighbors began gathering around doors and windows.

The two missionary couples soon had a Sunday school going. And while the Boyces worked in the clinic, the Woods flew out to mountain villages for evangelistic ministries.

From friendly townspeople Dr. Jim heard about an interesting missionary predecessor who had sold Bibles along the Mexican Pacific coast and in Ometepec. Captain Brinton, an English naval officer, was something of a hero in Mexico for having come at the joint request of Queen Victoria and the Mexican president to help the country build up its navy. After finishing his assignment, Captain Brinton had launched into missionary work.

On his last trip in 1921, he had walked from Acapulco to Ometepec, leading a burro loaded with Bibles. While in Ometepec he fell ill and died. His donkey was sold to pay funeral expenses, and the Bibles were given away.

One day a local dentist showed Dr. Jim a dusty black book. Dr. Jim's polite interest changed to excitement at the realization that this was Captain Brinton's faded personal Bible. As he turned the pages he was fascinated to read sentence prayers inscribed in the margins. Beside Psalm 2:8—"Ask of me, and I shall give thee the heathen for thine inheritance"—Captain Brinton had written, "O Lord, give me West Mexico for my inheritance."

Dr. Jim could scarcely contain his eagerness as he asked the dentist if he would accept a new Bible in exchange for the old one. The dentist agreed, and the Bible became Dr. Jim's prize possession.

The dentist had never read Captain Brinton's Bible. But he began reading the new Bible, and in time he, his wife, and a young telegraph operator boarding with them were among the Boyces' first converts. Later, the young boarder, Ignacio Castañeda, committed his life to the ministry and, after training in Mexico City, returned to Ometepec to become the first Mexican pastor of the Ometepec Evangelical Church. And the dentist became one of the first elders.

As more people began realizing that Dr. Jim was not "some kind of devil" as the fanatics claimed, his medical practice picked up. Intestinal parasites, diarrhea, tuberculosis, and malnutrition were the chief afflictions of the motley stream of patients who daily arrived at his door. Many were Amuzgo Indians from the mountains and Negroes from coastal villages who could not afford the other doctors in town. A few were afflicted with leprosy, which Dr. Jim had believed did not exist in the area.

His busiest time of the year for treating wounds was Holy Week. Four or five men were usually shot to death in drunken arguments and many others wounded. Domestic quarrels resulted in more knifings and shootings.

But at any time, Dr. Jim never knew what to expect from shootings resulting from feuds, land disputes, arguments over women, drunken brawls, and cattle stealing. Rustling was so frequent that a man bringing beef to market had to bring along the hide stamped with his brand. Hostilities were bad enough to warrant the stationing at Ometepec of a unit of soldiers ready to ride at a moment's notice.

Law required Dr. Jim to report all wounded patients to the general who commanded the unit. But one day when he gave the general a description of two wounded men recuperating in the clinic, he got an unexpected reaction. An incredulous look on his face, the general exclaimed, "Those two are mortal enemies. I'll send a guard down right now."

Periodically, the Army launched special crackdowns against the bandits who ambushed men for as little as a bucket of lard. One Sunday morning the town buzzed with news that ten men had been hung along various trails leading into Ometepec.

Fortunately for the Boyces, the tough general was aware that a few fanatics didn't want them in Ometepec. When he got the news one night that a band of men were heading for the doctor's

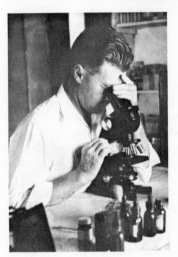

Above: Dr. James Boyce (wearing helmet) supervises delivery of man wounded in gunfight. **Left:** A one-doctor hospital requires the missionary physician to play many roles. Dr. Boyce, a Presbyterian missionary in Ometepec, Mexico, peers at a specimen through a gift microscope. (Presbyterian Church, U.S., photos)

home to burn it down, he immediately dispatched soldiers to handle the situation. They patrolled the street all night long while the Boyces, unaware of the danger, slept blissfully.

Except for his red hair and fair complexion, Dr. Jim could have passed for a mestizo. He had a small, neatly trimmed mustache, the trademark of most Mexican men. His size matched the customarily short stature of the local señores. He spoke Spanish fluently and learned some Amuzgo from Indian patients and the local Wycliffe translators. With the townsfolk, who appreciated his unselfish service at whatever patients could afford to pay, he enjoyed good rapport. He knew local merchants and

professional men on a first-name basis and helped organize the
Ometepec Lions Club. When the president of the Acapulco Lions
came down to present the Ometepec Lions a charter and learned
about Dr. Jim's medical work, he contributed money for needed
equipment. Later the Ometepec Lions elected Dr. Jim to serve
a term as their president.

In 1955 the Southern Presbyterian Board of Foreign Missions
allotted money to begin construction of a permanent 25-bed
hospital. But the earthquake of 1957 caused much damage and
Dr. Jim ran short of funds. A trip home to secure additional
Board aid was necessary before the brick-and-stone one-story
building could be finished. After the hospital was finally ready,
he added two Mexican doctors to the staff and began a nursing
school.

With staff help Dr. Jim felt he could spare time for visits
to rural villages, so he secured a used Piper Cub that could land
and take off on short strips. Within a flying radius of thirty
minutes, he lined up twenty-five spots, although some of the
landing fields were little more than cow pastures.

Twice weekly after loading in medicines and Bibles, he flew
to a rural community. Villagers flocked to a designated spot,
usually a building, but sometimes under a tree. There Dr. Jim
dispensed pills, gave shots, treated minor wounds, and asked
the seriously ill to come into the hospital. He customarily gave a
brief Bible reading and short evangelistic talk before loading
his bag and pay into the plane. When these country men worked,
they earned only about fifty cents a day; accordingly, Dr. Jim
was usually paid with chickens, eggs, and other produce. Perhaps the most unusual fee he ever received was a live four-foot
iguana (considered a delicacy by the Indians) which he took
home in the plane.

After one hard landing caused by structural failure of the
landing gear, Dr. Jim decided a new plane was needed. Rev.
Bill Christie, a Presbyterian pastor in Florida, sparked a cam-
paign among Presbyterian churches to give trading stamps for
a new plane. Literally tens of thousands of stamps were donated.
One package came with a grumbling note from a Louisiana
housewife: "Here they are, but this is worse than donating
blood."

The joy of having the new Piper Cub was cut short, however.
Soon after Dr. Jim flew it into Ometepec, Johnny and Madge
Wood took off in their old Cessna from Mexico City for Ometepec

in marginal weather and crashed a few minutes later on a mountainside.

The loss of their closest missionary friends put double work upon the Boyces. Dr. Jim had to assume leadership of the newly organized Ometepec Presbyterian Church until the national pastor who was finishing work at the Presbyterian seminary in Mexico City could take over.

The Boyces' closest brush with death came when an earthquake shook Ometepec one night shortly after they had arrived back from a furlough visit to the States. Two people were killed, but the Boyces suffered merely the inconvenience of having their still open suitcases filled with falling plaster.

Dr. Jim's only serious injury came when he fell on a roof while trying to remove a frightened kitten. A fractured vertebra and strained ligaments kept him in bed for a month. One day a former patient stopped by to see him. As she extended her artificial hand to give him his medicine, he thought of her condition when she had first come to the hospital. In a drunken rage her husband had sliced off both her hands and beaten her about the face with a machete. One of the Mexican staff doctors somehow managed to stop the gushing flow of blood and suture the wounds. Later Dr. Jim arranged for her to be admitted to the Rehabilitation Institute in Mexico City where she was given the artificial hook hands. When he asked her how she was getting along, she smiled and said, "I'm making a living for my children with my sewing machine."

Dr. Jim Boyce is fifty-four now. His red hair has dulled to yellow. Both he and Marguerite feel more at home in Mexico than in the United States. So do their five outstanding children, whom Marguerite taught at home (while also serving as the hospital's bookkeeper) until they were ready for high school.

James, Jr., the oldest, is completing his doctorate in physics at Duke University. Florence is a pastor's wife in San Antonio, Texas. Peggy is in Columbia Theological Seminary and interested in linguistics. Elizabeth is a college sophomore majoring in flute. Bill, the youngest, is a junior in a Chattanooga, Tennessee, prep school.

Once in a while Dr. Jim and Marguerite drive or fly to Acapulco and mingle with the affluent tourists and the townspeople.

On a recent trip their car was whistled to a stop by a traffic policeman. "What did I do wrong?" Dr. Jim asked the husky officer.

"Dr. Boyce, don't you remember me when I was skinny and sick?"

Dr. Jim looked hard at the big man. "Why, yes, you had tuberculosis."

"Look at me now," the officer said pushing out his chest. "You are one good doctor, Amigo."

3.

Never Too Old for Service

HOWARD HAMLIN, M.D.

The big jet roared off the runway at Johannesburg, South Africa, and bit into the murky air. Through holes in the clouds, the distinguished, graying Chicago surgeon could see the modern skyscrapers of the city—such a contrast to the primitive, brown bush country of Swaziland where he had served for a few weeks.

He sat busy with his thoughts as the plane climbed to its cruising altitude. The seat belt sign went dark, and the jet leveled off above the weather.

"Look happy, Howard," his wife said. "We're going home."

He looked at her and shrugged. "We'll enjoy seeing the grandchildren again. And our friends at church. But what else do we have to look forward to?" He paused and answered his own question. "Just to go back and collect more money.

"There are plenty of doctors in Chicago, Maxine," he continued. "But in Swaziland where we've been things are different. I really felt needed there."

Dr. Hamlin was recalling his summer's visit to Nazarene mission hospitals in Swaziland and the Transvaal region of South Africa. He had hardly arrived when he realized that the staff was terribly overworked. He had jumped in to help the mission doctors and nurses, often operating from eight o'clock one morning until two the following morning. One thing he discovered—he wasn't the iron man of medicine he once thought he had been. There in Swaziland he had almost become a "basket case" within three weeks.

The veteran surgeon wiped his eyes as he remembered the grateful thanks offered to him by a Swazi mother: "Doctor, we have cried Swazi tears for many years, but no one came from America to help. Now you have come."

But he hadn't stayed. The time for his departure was upon him all too soon. Back in Chicago he had schedules to meet, he told them. Patients were waiting for him there.

The jet hummed along far above the ocean. But the woman's words kept echoing in his mind. "Now you will help us . . . you will help us . . . "

He tried to think of his schedule ahead, but memories of the summer kept crowding in. Repeatedly, he asked himself some hard questions:

Why do the mission personnel have to work until exhausted?

Why is it that most of the mission dispensaries have no electric lights, running water, or sanitary facilities?

Why are antibiotics available only for the most desperately ill?

How can these problems be solved?

No matter how long or hard he thought, two simple answers to the last question kept coming back: money and people.

He had been trying to help with money—a tithe and more. But in view of what he had just seen in Swaziland, this didn't seem to be enough.

Should he, fifty-one years old and a grandfather, apply for permanent mission appointment? "They'd turn me down," he thought. "I'm too old."

Perhaps he might try a private practice near one of the mission hospitals. He could work for two days in his practice, then give three days a week to the hospital.

All the way home he thought about what he might do. But every idea seemed impractical.

Back in Chicago, Dr. Howard Hamlin resumed his busy, hectic life. He was chief of the Department of Surgeons at South Shore Hospital, a teacher in the Department of Surgery at the University of Illinois School of Medicine, vice-president and medical director of an insurance company, consultant surgeon for several large Chicago corporations. And there was his large private practice.

A dedicated churchman, he frequently took time off to speak to lay meetings. He taught a youth Sunday school class which often met for recreation in the basement of the Hamlin house near First Nazarene Church in Chicago. He had named the class himself—"Hamlin's Happy Heathen"—although he suspected a few church people had raised their eyebrows when they heard it. But no amount of church work could erase the growing concern he had for the missionary career he so desperately wanted.

His interest in foreign missions had never been a secret. Still, early in 1963, when the General Board of the Nazarene Church wrote, "Will you accept appointment as a permanent medical missionary to serve in Africa?" he could hardly believe it. Although (or perhaps, because) Dr. Hamlin was a longtime board member himself, he had never anticipated that an exception would be made in the age limit. But now his colleagues, knowing of his interest, by their decision had placed the future in his hands.

He never seriously considered saying no.

Those who were closest to him were not surprised when he and Mrs. Hamlin announced that they would be going back to Africa as permanent missionaries. His son-in-law, Rev. Dallas Mucci, noted, "He's always wanted to be a missionary. He's simply going in the footsteps of his father."

Howard Hamlin's carpenter father had certainly been mission-minded. When he moved his family to Beatrice, Nebraska, he reminded them of his motto, "Let George do it." Then he mortgaged his hogs, rented a vacant store building, and called for a pastor from a neighboring town to hold a revival meeting. Soon there was a congregation in Beatrice with the Hamlin family as the main backers. But George Hamlin didn't always follow his motto. He got his children involved in the janitoring, praying, and song-leading.

The family moved to Denver, Colorado, when Howard was a teenager. By this time he had caught the fire of his father's zeal. He and fifteen other teenagers organized the Mission Band of the First Nazarene Church. They moved about in an old truck and backed up evangelistic meetings with trumpets, trombones, and violins.

The Hamlin kind of religion included education. After high school graduation, Howard studied at the University of Colorado where he slaved in the college kitchen to defray expenses.

Howard soon became known for his stubborn convictions. He made good grades, but refused to "crack" a book on Sunday, even though this sometimes required rising at 4:00 A.M. on Monday to prepare for an exam.

He set his heart on medical school and made it. In his junior year, however, Howard's first "stitch job" revealed an unforeseen obstacle in his path. The patient was a waitress who had cut her finger on a broken glass. Trying to display professional poise, Howard injected a novocaine anesthetic, then began stitching while the waitress looked on in doubt. But he met with frustration when it was time to tie the thread. Again and again, he threw the looped thread over the needle holder, but without success. Her patience exhausted, the waitress cut him down by asking, "How are you making out, amateur?"

That was all he could take. Leaving the patient for an intern to finish, he slipped away to an easier task.

Discouraged, he realized he had to learn to stitch if he was to ever do surgery. But when would he find the time to practice?

Refusing to admit defeat, he practiced on the streetcar as he went to and from classes. He would slip a piece of string through a buttonhole in his coat and practice tying surgical knots. He worked until he could tie the knots blindfolded.

After interning at Baltimore City Hospital under staff members from famed Johns Hopkins and the University of Maryland medical schools, he asked the Nazarene General Board to appoint him to China. But a revolution inside the populous country made the assignment impossible. He enlisted in the Army in 1944 and asked to be sent to the Orient.

In Tokyo he was assigned as assistant chief of the surgical service at the 42nd General Hospital, the highest echelon of medical service in the Far Eastern Command. Later he was transferred to be a consultant to General Douglas MacArthur's headquarters group. In this job, which was primarily geared to rehabilitation of public health among the Japanese, Dr. Hamlin helped write policy for the occupied nation on drug vaccine and controls. The extensive travel over all four main Japanese islands (plus Okinawa and Korea) in connection with his work alerted Dr. Hamlin to the need for more hospitals there.

While still on General MacArthur's staff he suggested to the Nazarene Board that the denomination build a mission hospital in Japan. But they could take no action. Budgets were tight and personnel was not available to staff a hospital in those immediate postwar years.

Still burdened for the Japanese, Dr. Hamlin fervently presented his idea for a mission hospital at a banquet held in the Headquarters Chapel Center and hosted by the Army chief of chaplains. The stony silence that greeted him at the end of his plea convinced him that he had failed.

A painful interval passed. Then a veteran representative of a large mission board stood and, with evident emotion, said, "Mr. Chairman, not until tonight did I realize how much we as Protestants have failed to meet our missionary obligations to Japan. We are not a legislative body, but I move that we take whatever steps are necessary to get Dr. Hamlin and this message to the World Council of Churches in New York." This request was answered with thunderous applause.

Two months later, from the secretary to the Committee on Medical Missions for the World Council Dr. Hamlin received a telegram inviting him to New York. Here he learned that several denominations were joining together to sponsor the Christian University in Tokyo. It would include a medical school of which they wanted him to become dean. He could choose his own faculty and set the school's policies.

In declining the honor, Dr. Hamlin said simply, "I wish to be a surgeon, not an administrator." Then he moved to Chicago to complete his specialty board examinations.

From 1949 to 1963 Dr. Hamlin enjoyed a busy surgical practice in Chicago. He became a nationally known layman in his Nazarene denomination and served in several leadership posts.

His fellow Nazarenes quickly came to enjoy his sense of humor. Members who served with him on the General Board of the denomination have not forgotten the occasion when he took advantage of a Board recess to hang pictures of dogs in the hall of the conference building. Under each dog he scribbled the name of a board member. The churchmen returned to find themselves classified as bulldogs, beagles, French poodles, and other assorted breeds. When the chairman reconvened the meeting, he announced in mock solemnity, "We have no doubt about the person who committed this foul deed."

No one ever charged Howard Hamlin with selfishness. In fact a member of his family said, "We have to watch that he doesn't take too much on a trip. He will give it all away before he gets home."

Patients knew him as "the praying doctor." One morning he was making rounds at Presbyterian Hospital and met the night nurse in the corridor.

"How is Mrs. _____?" he asked. "You know, the one who is dying of cancer."

"She's been delirious since I came on duty," the nurse replied. "Keeps saying that you came down here last night about midnight and prayed for her."

"Well, I did," the surgeon told the surprised nurse.

But despite all the satisfactions of a busy surgeon's life, he never lost the yearning to be a full-time foreign missionary. When Dallas Mucci had asked permission to marry his daughter Sandy, Dr. Hamlin agreed and then said, "Somehow, God is kindly easing the hurt by the fact that Sandy will share in the work of a pastor. I rejoice with you. Right now, I would swap my Cadillac for a bicycle if the church would send me to the mission field."

There was a ripple of surprise among doctor friends, however, when word got around in Chicago that he was resigning his practice and other various positions and going to Africa permanently. A Jewish surgeon read the story in the *Chicago Tribune* and phoned. "I always figured something was wrong with you, Howard," he said jokingly. "Why are you doing this?"

"For the same reason that one of your greatest forebears became a missionary," Dr. Hamlin replied. "As Paul said, 'The love of Christ constraineth me.' "

The two got together and talked. After Dr. Hamlin described the need of the mission hospitals, his Jewish friend donated a large stock of expensive instruments. So did a medical manufacturer for which Dr. Hamlin had served as consulting surgeon.

Before leaving, Dr. Hamlin and his wife, Maxine, spoke to their home church.

"Why eighteen years have had to elapse since the door closed to China, I will never know," he said. "Perhaps a seasoning process was necessary; perhaps we needed a few courses in the school of experience, perhaps God was avoiding a tragedy. But after visiting Africa and working in our hospitals there, I knew I could never again complacently return to my comfortable life. Prayer that God would stir others to give, and to go, could never again substitute for my personal action. Giving money could never again be the measure of my stewardship responsibility."

He paused and looked at his children: first at Sandy, sitting beside her preacher husband; then at his other daughter, Karen, and at his son, Kim, both students in Eastern Nazarene College.

"We'll miss the warmth of our children's and grandchildren's caresses and the fun of their lives. But the call of God must hold priority above these cherished relationships."

The Hamlins kissed their loved ones goodbye and left for Johannesburg, South Africa. From there they drove to their main station, the 300-bed Raleigh Fitkin Hospital in Manzini, Swaziland.

"The junior missionaries have arrived," Dr. Hamlin declared to his younger colleagues upon reaching his destination. "Where's the operating room?" But almost before he could get started he came down with hepatitis.

After a few weeks he recovered and plunged into his work. Besides superintending and operating at the Swaziland hospital, he was assigned to spend one week out of every month at the Church of the Nazarene's hospital in the Transvaal region of South Africa. The two hundred and fifty miles of road between the two mission hospitals was bouncy and always unpredictable during the rainy season. And he soon learned that the idea of sharing time between the hospitals was a joke because each staff saved up cases while he was at the other hospital.

At the Swaziland hospital he found himself working nights and Saturdays to stay caught up with administrative paper work. In handling the purchasing he had to keep the eye of a hawk on prices quoted by suppliers. Once he challenged the price of 55 rand (about $75) for a thousand doses of Chloromycetin, a powerful antibiotic especially effective against resistant germs. "But we're charging the corporation doctors 120 rand," the salesman retorted.

Howard Hamlin's eyes flashed. "You're still charging us too much. We're not here to make money. We're here to help people who can't get aid elsewhere." The salesman relented and dropped the price to 12.5 rand.

When the Hamlins arrived in 1963, Swaziland (6,705 square miles; population, 395,139) was a British protectorate, although the tiny nation gained independence in 1968. British officials appointed Dr. Hamlin consulting surgeon at the government hospital twenty-five miles from the mission hospital. In fact, he was the only Board-certified surgeon in all of Swaziland.

At the Raleigh Fitkin Hospital, Dr. Hamlin installed a central address system with speakers in each ward for broadcasting a devotional service three times daily. The surgeon tried to explain to each patient through an interpreter, "I'm like a man who prunes the bad limbs off a tree as I take out diseased tissue.

God's power does the healing." But because of the number of
surgical cases (one year at Fitkin the five Nazarene missionary
doctors did 950 major and 2,000 minor operations) it was difficult for him to spend much time with a patient. He lamented to
a colleague, "We see so many people that we never can give a
meaningful witness for Christ."

He learned to get along without ultramodern equipment, and
he had to handle cases that in Chicago he would have sent to
sub-specialists. Once he removed a lung tumor without aid of
intravenous fluids or blood transfusions, and with only one
nurse to assist. In five years he saw just one gallstone patient,
in contrast to the hundreds of stones he had removed in Chicago.
"Gallstones," he told a missionary, "are part of the price Americans pay for eating rich food."

Another time he was removing a bead from a child's lung
when the lights failed. He closed the bronchus and lung under
the beam of a flashlight held by a student nurse.

The number of ulcer cases was surprising. Dr. Hamlin noted
they were mainly among Africans who had become involved in
business, teaching, and other European type occupations. However, several of the ulcerated stomachs he looked into belonged
to native chiefs who were suffering from the pressures of detribalization and loss of authority as civilization pressed in. He
did numerous pyloroplasties, a common operation where the
passageway from the stomach to the duodenum is broadened to
relieve ulcerated constriction of the far end of the stomach,
combining it with a vagotomy—the severing of the vagus nerve
to stop secretion of acid in the stomach.

One of his most thrilling cases was that of an old chief who
came to the hospital weak from loss of blood and expecting to
die. After the surgical staff had built him up with massive blood
transfusions, Dr. Hamlin opened his stomach and found a huge
gastric ulcer. He did a gastric resection, removing a large portion of the stomach. The chief recovered and resumed his duties.
Soon a steady stream of patients began arriving from the chief's
tribe for treatment. Many became Christians and a new church
was established in the tribe, although the chief himself never
made a profession of faith.

During his first term, Dr. Hamlin found two specialized areas
of his past training and experience invaluable. In the Army
Medical Corps, he had specialized in surgery on the peripheral
nerves. This skill he used at all three hospitals to restore several

Dr. Howard Hamlin, distinguished surgeon
and lay leader in the Church of the Nazarene,
became the oldest candidate ever to
be appointed by his mission board.

Dr. Hamlin
takes medicine
to the people in
Swaziland.

Dr. Hamlin holds
a roadside clinic.

Moment of triumph and worship
comes when a Swaziland nurse is capped
at the Nazarene Nursing College in Swaziland.
(Church of the Nazarene photo)

accident cases to normalcy with tendon transplants. One was a member of the royal family.

While doing his surgical residency at Presbyterian St. Luke's Hospital in Chicago, he and three other doctors had pioneered in using a saecal, or substitute bladder. The procedure (for which each team member won a gold medal from the American Urological Association) involved transplanting a patient's urinary stream into a temporary bladder built from a section of intestine while repairing the diseased urinary tract. The method worked wonders in Africa on new mothers who came in with bladders torn from trying to give birth in the bush.

Maxine Hamlin had always been an active churchwoman. At the Swaziland mission hospital she took charge of the central supply of non-medical materials. She kept nurses, technicians, and other hospital employees in uniforms. She mended, sorted, and distributed used clothing given by Nazarenes in the United States and Canada. But her favorite task was distributing wedding and bridal gowns sent by home missionary societies for African girls.

Both Howard and Maxine Hamlin learned to respect and admire the Africans in their emergence from primitive living and long centuries of colonial rule. Dr. Hamlin recognized that the witch doctors' treatments were not all "hocus-pocus." They helped heart problems with digitalis, relaxed colic and bowel spasms with atrophine, and stopped excess secretions of glands with belladonna. They also prescribed lion fat and bat dung for various ailments, two remedies Dr. Hamlin judged unscientific.

In 1968, shortly before the end of their first term, Dr. Hamlin traveled north to hold evangelistic meetings in Lourenço Marques, the capital of Portuguese Mozambique. After an evening service a well-dressed, smiling Portuguese couple invited him and fellow missionary Floyd Perkins out for ice cream.

"Doctor, you never met me before, but I've seen you," their host said in the ice cream parlor. "Remember that train wreck in Swaziland about two years ago?"

Dr. Hamlin nodded. "Yes, I was called out of bed about 5:00 A.M. We got there on a hand car and worked for hours with the dead and injured."

"I was the highest ranking Portuguese official on that train. I watched you work. The next week my little daughter suddenly fell ill and my wife asked me, 'Where can we take her?' I said

immediately, 'Let's go to the mission hospital down in Swaziland
and see that doctor who helped at the train wreck.' "

His eyes moist, the Portuguese continued. "Doctor, you were
not at the hospital when we arrived. Another missionary doctor
took care of my little girl. He prayed over her before surgery.
The operation was successful.

"We came back to Mozambique but could not forget that
prayer. I had never heard a doctor ask for God's help before.
Finally we looked for a church that was associated with your
hospital in Swaziland. We found one here in Lourenço Marques
where we heard the gospel."

The man swallowed hard. "We were both converted and found
the greatest happiness we ever knew. Now God has called me
to the ministry and I'm planning to attend a seminary."

Looking straight into Dr. Hamlin's eyes, the Portuguese man
whispered, "Thank you, Doctor, for coming out to that train
wreck."

Later, while on furlough in the United States, Howard Hamlin
told three hundred Christian doctors gathered for the 1969 International Convention on Missionary Medicine, "The past five
years has showed me some things about missionary medicine.
We can't separate evangelism from medicine if we're going to
be Christian doctors. We can't treat everybody, nor should we
try to run competition with government health programs. I
think we'll always be limited in the number of cases we can
handle.

"I'm not sure any more that the big mission hospital is the
best answer. Visits with patients can become too hurried and
impersonal. A network of dispensaries can help us take medicine
and the gospel to the people. If we have a hospital, it should
only be for people who need specialized treatment."

He paused and surveyed his audience of doctors, many of
whom were furloughing missionaries like himself. "Back at the
University of Colorado I played the tuba in the band. For one
concert we played the melody called 'Whistler and His Dog.' At
the appropriate time it was my responsibility to bark. If I
hadn't barked well that night, the music would not have been
complete.

"The missionary work of the church is like a great symphony.
Each of us has an instrument and some music that fits into the
overall plan. My assignment in the divine symphony took me to
Africa at fifty-two. Looking back, I'm not sure that I accom-

plished much in tangible results. But I never doubted that God wanted me there."

He told the doctors about the Portuguese man who had seen him helping at the train wreck. "I didn't operate on the man's daughter. I didn't even explain the gospel to him. But I was at the train wreck where he saw my witness of service.

"God willing, I hope to give ten more years in Africa." He paused and chuckled. "Right after I came home from furlough I went through the indignities of a two-day physical at the Lahey Clinic in Boston. They looked me over from stem to stern. Then I did what we doctors don't like our patients to do. I looked at my chart and saw that some doctor had written this appraisal: 'For an old man, he's in pretty good condition.' "

When his audience stopped laughing, Dr. Hamlin added, "Let's not leave all the missionary work to the young man. God has something for us old fogies to do, too."

4.

Lady Doctor of the Jungle

NEVA WIESEKE, M.D.

Wrapped in a loin cloth, the Chacabo Indian stands meekly before a pretty, dark-haired young woman. He is wearing the latest fashions of his tribe: parrot feathers protrude through his nose cartilage, toucan feathers crown his braided hair, his ears are pierced by curved rodent incisors, and a bark dress rustles around his ankles. If you were a neophyte explorer trekking through Bolivia's hot and humid northern jungles and were to come upon this scene, you would think you were watching the filming of a Tarzan drama.

The young woman shatters your illusions by informing you she is not Jane, but Neva Wieseke—Doctor Wieseke, to be exact. And, since she isn't married, there's no Tarzan.

Next you wonder, *What's a young lady doctor with a complexion good enough for a bath soap commercial doing in the jungle with only her medicine bag for protection?*

With a girlish smile and an all-business tone of voice, the 33-year-old lady medico tells you she is doing a community health study. Pointing to a naked boy who stands behind her patient, she says, "See that distended stomach? Parasites. I can temporarily de-worm him and the whole tribe with a mass administration of hexylresorcinol medication. But that is not a permanent solution. In fact, there's not so much a worm problem here as a sanitation and water pollution problem with its attendant bacterial and gastrointestinal afflictions."

"Well," you ask facetiously, "why don't you call the sanitation department and get a crew out here?"

The soft face firms. Apparently she doesn't appreciate your humor. She motions to a white man and his wife who have just emerged from a hut. "The linguists are the sanitation department out here. They're trying to get the Indians to build and use latrines and not to drink unboiled water. But the linguists can't overnight change practices that have been followed for centuries."

You decide to hang around and watch Dr. Wieseke at work. She inspects each villager for parasitic diseases, does a physical exam, checks vital signs, tests for tuberculosis ("a common malady," she says), and jots down information on punched IBM cards. Then she completes a questionnaire by walking around the village and asking leading questions of the inhabitants. She notes the type of houses they live in, whether or not the houses have walls, if the sleeping area is off the ground, what pets the family may have and if the pets run through the huts freely, whether mosquito nets are used, where the family goes to the bathroom, and where they get their water supply.

She asks the adults what children have died, at what ages and for what reasons. A third have died before reaching sixteen, she discovers. She queries the men about previous wives who have died. One toothless man has lost four wives, all from tuberculosis. What she finds when she glances at his card confirms her suspicions: he is a carrier of the disease. "Almost certainly he gave it to the wives," she declares, "and they were not strong enough to resist the disease."

Upon finishing the questionnaire, she makes suggestions to the linguist and his wife, who, she says, must be involved with medical work whether they like it or not. "They live with the people and must play the leading role in getting them to change disease-producing hygiene and sanitation habits. By translating the New Testament and living a Christian life of service, they're helping to break up old superstitions and taboos. It's hard to get Indians who believe disease is caused by evil spirits to see that their daily living habits are to blame."

Now, you believe, you understand what a missionary jungle doctor does. "Not altogether," Dr. Wieseke informs you. "This is just part of what I do. Come along to the base on the plane that will be here to pick me up this afternoon."

At first you hear only the hum of the engine above the canopy of 200-foot-high trees. Then suddenly you see the shimmer of silver as the pilot banks for the right landing angle on the narrow strip. The little single-engine Helio Courier is a welcome sight as it bounces to a stop. You follow the doctor on board, and moments later the plane is soaring above the green carpet that stretches endlessly toward all horizons. You try not to think of what could happen if the engine fails. You glance at the lady doctor strapped in the copilot's seat. She is fast asleep.

An hour later the pilot is over the base, whose towering palms make it look much like a hideaway community in Florida. The lake that curves beside the dozen or so homes rushes up to meet the plane. Now the plane is down and you are taxiing toward shore where a small crowd of children and adults are waving greetings.

After a good night's sleep under the rustle of the palms and the pounding of jungle rain on a tin roof, followed by a hearty bacon and eggs breakfast, you want to see what the doctor has on her day's agenda. As you walk toward the base clinic, the melody of "Home on the Range" carries through a grove of banana trees. The children are singing their school song to the familiar tune.

> O give me a home where the animals roam,
>   In Bolivian jungles so wild,
> With a school by the lake, where teachers all take
>   An int'rest in each questioning child.
> Tu-mi Chucua* School,
> The school that we all love so well,
> Where we study and play at the right time each day,
>   And endeavor to follow God's way.

"I'm the only doctor for this American community of about a hundred adults and children," the doctor tells you. "About one-third of the adults are Bible translators working in fifteen tribes. The rest are pilots, mechanics, teachers, secretaries, publications people and so on. They consult me just as they would their family doctor back home, but without charge, of course. I'm just one member of a team that's working to reach a goal of a New Testament for every tribal language. This, naturally, involves much more than writing down their language and then translating the Bible. After all, what good is a translation if the people can't read and write, or, even worse, if they aren't alive to read it?"

You meet various members of the team as they come in for

_____
*Pronounced *Too me chooquah*

Dr. Neva Wieseke treks through the Amazon jungle to a tribe where she will do a community health study. (Wycliffe Bible Translators photo)

Dr. Douglas Swanson of the Wycliffe Bible Translators in Peru inoculates an Indian village against an epidemic of measles. (Wycliffe Bible Translators photo)

appointments. One most interesting fellow is Gil Prost, linguist to the Chacobos. You listen and learn about his community development program and a recent clinic conducted there by Dr. Wieseke.

Fifteen years ago the Chacobos were known only as an elusive and diminishing shadow people who had fled deep into the jungles to escape advancing white colonists. In 1955, the year Wycliffe entered Bolivia at the personal invitation of President Paz Estenssoro, Gil Prost and colleague Perry Priest discovered a Chacobo settlement. A few weeks later Gil and his young wife Marian moved into the corner of a big communal lodge, living there until their own house was thatched. Subsequently, the Prosts moved the entire tribe of 170 to a more productive land site which he had surveyed and to which he had obtained title from the government for the Chacobos. But the Indians, whose numbering system had been limited to "one, two, and others," were slow to respond to the message of Mark's Gospel which Gil translated. Not until the Prosts' tenth year did the first man, a chief, refuse to partake in the traditional service to the "yo-shini," the "prince of the evil spirits." Two years later, when Dr. Wieseke held the community clinic and health study in the tribe, there were about twenty converts.

You look over Dr. Wieseke's shoulder as she thumbs through her records of that visit. "They were in better condition than some tribes," she recalls. "They had not been exposed to measles, so we gave them measles vaccine. Tuberculosis wasn't nearly as widespread as I found elsewhere. The Christians were very co-operative but those who had not broken with spirit worship still preferred the old ways." She stops and looks at Gil. "Remember that little girl of about eighteen months and the witch doctor who started the death wail while I was working on her?"

Gil grins. "Yes. He had built a fire under her hammock, which they do when somebody is sick, and had been rubbing her with leaves and blowing on her abdomen. But she got well and he takes our medicine now for tuberculosis."

"That's an illustration of what I tried to tell you yesterday," Dr. Wieseke tells you. "We find that instead of modern medicine preparing the way for the gospel, the gospel prepares the people to trust in our remedies."

That afternoon the Wycliffe children start coming in for im-munizations. "School will be out in a few weeks," Dr. Wieseke explains, "and many of them will be going back to their own villages with their parents. We not only want to protect them but also to protect the Indians from them. The white man's diseases can decimate a village of people who have not built up an immunity."

The next day you find Dr. Wieseke checking the manuscript of a health book with a pair of linguists who are preparing it for their people. Then she has a small class of Indian young men who at the base are studying to become government certified teachers. After class she tells you, "This is part of our program of training Indian leaders to teach school and do community development work, which includes medicine. We now have several bilingual schools where children become literate in their own languages before moving on to Spanish."

Outside there is a buzz of excitement as a Wycliffe plane lands with an official from La Paz, the Bolivian capital. A few minutes later he enters the clinic and asks to meet Dr. Wieseke. When introduced to the stylish young woman, he looks past her at first. Upon realizing that she is Dr. Wieseke, he apologizes profusely. "Ah, I did not expect to see such a lovely *doctora*," he says as he leans forward to kiss her hand.

After the official has left, Dr. Wieseke mentions that the Bolivian government contributes $100 a month to Wycliffe's medical program. "This isn't a large amount by U.S. standards," she admits, "but it is a lot for a landlocked country where the per capita annual income is only $142 per person.

"Now let's see," she muses. "Monday, I fly out to another tribe for a community health study. I'll be there for a couple of weeks if you'd like to come along."

You decline politely and wonder, just wonder, if Dr. Wieseke doesn't miss the affluent living other doctors are enjoying back home. "Not really," she says, with a toss of curls. "I get wrapped up in the work here and forget about fancy clothes, food, parties, and all the things that they say should make you happy." She stops and punches out the next sentence with emphasis. "I don't believe they do, though. You're happiest when you're fulfilling the purpose God has for your life—whether in the United States or down here in one of the poorest countries on earth."

Before leaving, you inquire a bit into Dr. Wieseke's background to discover how she acquired this philosophy.

You learn she is of German stock from the small town of Marshall, Minnesota, west of Minneapolis and near the South

Dakota border. "Quite a difference in climate there and here," she observes with a smile.

She became a Christian in a Congregational church and graduated from the University of Minnesota Medical School at twenty-five, intending to be a missionary doctor. She took a year's internship and another year's residency in internal medicine at Gorgas Hospital in Panama, because, she says, "I wanted the chance to see what tropical medicine is like. But after several weekend trips into the interior, I realized that simply dishing out pills and shots for parasites was unsatisfying. I saw that living patterns would have to change if treatment was to have any lasting effect.

"I had written to one mission board and found nothing to get very excited about. One Sunday afternoon a friend asked if I would give her a ride to a house where a visiting missionary doctor was showing slides of his work. I took her and stayed to see them too. That's how I first learned about Wycliffe.

"Ralph Eichenberger from Wycliffe's base in Peru showed the slides. His community approach to health problems was what especially interested me. He talked about Wycliffe's team concept and how nutrition, sanitation, agriculture, vocational training, and literacy were all involved in a ministry to the whole man that centered in Bible translation."

"And after that?" you ask.

"I studied a semester at Columbia Bible College, then took the Wycliffe linguistics course at the University of North Dakota. After they accepted me as a member, I went through the jungle survival training camp in central Mexico, then came to Peru in 1965 for a few months before coming on here. I arrived just after Ralph Eichenberger left for an extended furlough. I did there much of what I'm doing here—community health studies, taking care of Wycliffe people, training Indian teachers. Nothing dramatic, but all very satisfying."

The shadows are deepening and the jungle night is fast descending as you leave the clinic where Dr. Wieseke still has more work to do. You compare her with the highly trained young professional people you know. Suddenly you realize the difference. Her life is, as she says, ". . . all very satisfying."

5.

Doctor of Yemen

JAMES M. YOUNG, JR., M.D.

The patients in the men's examining room look like characters from the *Arabian Nights*. The intense faces under the turbans range from light olive to dark brown or black. Most wear a skirt gathered at the waist by a leather belt. Under the belt is a jambiya, a large curved dagger. But one man cradles a rifle, another sits on a machine gun, and a youth with dark hair falling from under his turban holds a transistor radio to his ear—all symbols of the present era in the volatile Middle East.

The slim American doctor with short-cropped black hair specked with gray looks out of place as he moves among the Yemeni men. The man with the rifle has a broken arm—from a fall on the mountainside, he claims. Dr. James M. Young, Jr., ushers him into another room and tells him not to eat or drink anything for the next two hours so he can be given anesthesia. He returns and prescribes tablets from the pharmacy for another man who appears to have pulmonary tuberculosis. A third says he has no pain, but has brought his son for worm medicine. While Mrs. Young prepares prescriptions, the doctor talks excitedly about problems in his community.

A Spanish missionary nurse calls from the doorway. Will the doctor examine a pregnant woman? Telling the man he will be back soon, Dr. Young hurries to the women's examining room. The woman in question appears trim. The doctor asks in Arabic, "How long have you been with child?"

"Seven years," she replies solemnly.

42

Neither doctor nor nurse laughs. They know that Yemeni women often feign pregnancy to keep their husbands from divorcing them. The doctor prescribes a few pills and turns away. The nurse smiles and says, "Yes, and when he's born, he'll have a full set of teeth and be wearing a jambiya."

On his way back to the men's room, Dr. Young stops to see a bedfast patient. He is a minor government official who wants to talk about the differences between Muslim and Christian beliefs. The doctor, careful not to criticize the national religion, speaks softly and precisely. He realizes that he is permitted to serve in Yemen because he is a doctor, not because he is a Christian missionary.

Six years ago Dr. Young and his wife, June, moved to Yemen from Gaza to become the first resident missionaries in this fabled country for over thirteen hundred years.

Yemen and Ethiopia, which now face each other across the southwest and southeast shores of the Red Sea, once formed most of the land of Sheba. The Queen of Sheba traveled over twelve hundred and fifty miles from her capital of Marib in present Yemen to Jerusalem. Her camel train carried gifts of spices, gold, and precious stones for King Solomon (I Kings 10:2). A tradition says a son she bore by Solomon founded the ruling dynasty of Ethiopia from which the present King Haile Selassie descends.

During Solomon's era (about 950 B.C.), Yemen was one of the world's greatest civilizations. The great dam near Marib was one of the wonders of the world, matching the pyramids of Egypt. The dam supplied irrigation water for agricultural products and gardens that equalled any in the world. The Koran says the dam broke in 66 B.C. because the people forgot God. Today Marib is only a small village existing on a high mound of archaeological remains.

From about the seventh century, Yemen belonged to the Muslim world. A line of priest kings called "imams" (the first imam is said to have been the Prophet Mohammed) sought to maintain a tightly knit democracy, although at times various foreign nations held political control over the small country. Under the proverb "Progress comes from Allah," the imams taught Yemenis to accept every life situation as the divine will. The Muslim religion formed the sole basis for civil law. The land where telephones, railways, water systems, printing presses, and automobiles were banned became literally a "Kingdom of Silence."

Even the word for innovation, *bida*, in the religious sense also meant heresy, or something generally bad.

Suddenly a revolution in 1962 catapulted "the Silent Nation" into the modern world of rapid change. Public education, health, and modernization became vital concerns. Ambitious secularists pushed the idea that man could shape his own social future.

Dr. Young had been serving the Baptist Hospital in Gaza since 1955 and had built a reputation in the Arab world for unselfish service. Egypt's President Nasser had personally commended him for staying at his post during the 1956 Suez Canal crisis when all other Americans in Gaza were evacuated. Now aware of the changes beginning in Yemen, he hitched a ride in a United Nations plane to that country.

In Yemen he met with Ahmed Mohanny, then director general of the Ministry of Health. Mohanny had studied in the United States and was most interested in the possibility of having a Baptist hospital built in Yemen. In November 1963, the Muslim official wrote to the Southern Baptist Foreign Mission Board, "The health promotion of the people of Yemen is one of the outstanding aims of our young republican government. I cannot suggest any specific activities to be performed by you in Yemen, but Dr. Young's views and recommendations of what you could help with will be accepted by us."

In March 1964, Dr. Young returned to Yemen, accompanied by John D. Hughey, his board's secretary for Europe and the Middle East. They conferred with Mohanny and other officials. Mohanny smilingly said that the Yemenis were strong Muslims but hospitable and tolerant to people of other faiths. He added, "We are so much in need of medical care that we cannot be very discriminating."

At that time there was not one Yemeni doctor in the nation, although some aspirants had accepted training scholarships in Russia, Czechoslovakia, Rumania, and East Germany.

That same year Dr. and Mrs. Young and a Spanish Baptist nurse, Maria Luisa Hidalgo, opened a clinic in an unused wing of the government hospital at Taiz. With a population of 40,000, Taiz was the country's second largest city, and its hospital was one of three in the country. They had two wards—in effect, a 20-bed hospital. Dr. Young was given the privilege of operating once a week in the government hospital—provided he brought his own supplies and equipment. The license of his car, when translated from Arabic to English, read, "The Baptist Society, Taiz No. 1."

Yemenis flocked to the clinic from the town and surrounding dusty hills. Some were wounded victims of the continuing civil war between the revolutionary government and royalist forces who were entrenched further back in the mountains. Sometimes bomb blasts could be heard in Taiz from distant mountains, and occasionally a bomb exploded in Taiz itself.

From examining hundreds of patients, Dr. Young concluded the most prevalent diseases to be bilharzia (a parasitic disease often causing permanent liver damage), tuberculosis, and diarrhea of infancy and childhood. All were related to poor sanitation and hygiene—legacies of centuries of isolation from the outside world. Appendicitis, high blood pressure, and hardening of the arteries seldom seemed to occur.

At this time foreign technicians from both East and West were flooding into Taiz. Under the shadows of ancient fortified towers Chinese and Russian Communists rubbed shoulders with U.S. Agency for International Development workers.

When the Youngs started weekly worship services for the American families in Taiz, officials made no objection since no Yemenis attended the services. The Youngs and the Spanish nurse had opportunities for witness, however, when Yemenis asked them why they had come to Taiz and how they could believe in three gods instead of one.

During the summer of 1966, Dr. Z. W. Hutcheson, Jr., came from Texas under the Southern Baptist medical volunteer program to assist Dr. Young for a month. One afternoon when he was downtown taking pictures, a turbaned Yemeni approached and ordered, "Come with me to my office." The turbaned man turned out to be the police chief.

Questioned about what he was doing in Yemen, the visiting Texan said, "I'm working with Dr. Young."

The chief smiled. "Dr. Young is my friend. Take my picture if you wish."

Because of the large government hospital in Taiz, Dr. Young let it be known that he was interested in building a hospital where there was greater need. A response came from a leading sheik who was also the mayor of Jibla, a town to the north of Taiz and once the capital of the country. The sheik invited the Youngs and their Texas guests to a sumptuous feast in his Jibla palace. He also asked to see an Arabic Bible.

The town of Jibla could have come from the pages of a story-book. Marked by mosques and ancient fortresses, it even included a queen's palace dating to the eleventh century. As the missionaries came near, they saw a crowd of people pushing forward to meet them.

In the crowd were the sheik mayor and some of his men, all of whom were dressed in white with fancy daggers in their belts and carrying rifles slung across their shoulders. After greetings and a shooting demonstration, the missionaries followed the sheik and his party along an ageless cobblestone path toward a palace on the mountainside. Behind them, people trailed in single file as far back as they could see.

When they reached the palace, they entered the ancient door and climbed several flights of stairs. At a dark landing they removed their shoes and went into a room covered with a thick oriental carpet. More carpets hung on the wall.

The sheik waved them to seats on luxurious cushions where he served Pepsi-Cola and orange drink. Dr. Young gave the sheik the Arabic Bible which he had requested and the two began a long religious discussion in Arabic. Later they feasted on broiled chicken and roast lamb, scooping up vegetables with pancake-shaped fried bread.

The Southern Baptist Foreign Mission Board allotted funds for hospital facilities to be built on a terraced hillside overlooking the town. A 100-year lease was signed for the land, and a contract was given to a Swedish Christian builder. While on-site construction progressed, the medical team, bolstered by the arrival of three new missionary nurses, received patients in the clinic.

Local residents who had never known Christians before showed no animosity. One told Dr. Young, "We are glad you are here instead of the Chinese and Russian atheists. You believe in God."

The June 1967 Arab–Israeli war erupted while the hospital was still under construction. Diplomatic relations were broken between Yemen and the United States, and all Americans left the country except the Baptist missionaries at Jibla who continued treating the sick.

In March 1968, the well-equipped hospital complex was dedicated before a festive crowd of five hundred. Official guests included the governors of Taiz and of Ibb Province, the ministers of finance and health, army officers, sheiks, representatives of

Dr. James M. Young, Jr.,
Southern Baptist missionary doctor,
opened up the fabled land of Sheba
for the gospel with medicine.
(Southern Baptist Foreign
Mission Board photo)

Southern Baptists
in Gaza
have scored
dramatic breakthrough
in winning converts
through medical witness.
Here Dr. and Mrs. Merrill D.
Moore, Jr., talk to Muslim
outside hospital gate.
(Southern Baptist
Foreign Mission Board photo)

foreign embassies and of the World Health Organization, and Swedish, Italian, Russian, and Yemeni doctors.

Dr. Baker James Cauthen, executive secretary of the Southern Baptist Foreign Mission Board, told the audience that the hospital was a symbol of concern and an expression of love, made possible by the gifts of people who love God and want to reach out to others in kindness and helpfulness.

"This institution is significant because it calls attention to spiritual and eternal values of life," the veteran missionary executive said. "The illnesses of our bodies need attention, but the spiritual nature of man needs to be nourished and strengthened also. Jesus said, 'I am come that they might have life, and that they might have it more abundantly.' As people look to God in faith they find strength and encouragement to face what life brings."

Yemenis thronged to the hospital. Some walked for days through the dusty mountains to reach the oasis of mercy. Sheiks and government officials came from afar just to marvel at the facilities. Strangely, the hospital kitchen seemed to impress visitors the most, perhaps because in a Yemeni home the kitchen is the smallest and darkest room.

One wing of the H-shaped hospital contained wards and rooms for seventy beds. The other wing housed the operating area, central supply, nursing office, library, and kitchen. Two long 16x100-foot buildings had facilities for outpatients—examining rooms, operating room for minor surgery, pharmacy, laboratory, x-ray, etc. A large, low utility building contained power facilities, employee recreation room, storeroom, and morgue.

When furlough time came for the Youngs, Dr. David Dorr from the Baptist Hospital in Gaza arrived to take charge. As they were preparing to leave, Dr. Young explained to the local mayor-sheik that they wanted to see their oldest son, Bruce, a premedical student at Louisiana Polytechnic Institute, and enter their second son, Mark, as a sophomore in the same school. The sheik congratulated Dr. Young on his two boys who had attended high school in the Arab world. Characteristic of Arab men, the sheik had less to say about the Youngs' two teenage daughters who were still in high school.

The Youngs spent the 1969–70 school year in their native Louisiana. During that time Dr. Young, although busy preparing for his Board certification in surgery, and his wife frequently spoke to church groups. Dr. Young recalled for their audiences how

God had prepared them from childhood to be medical missionaries.

After his father died when he was only three, James Young had lived with his maternal grandparents. They took him to the Baptist church in Choudrant, Louisiana, every Sunday. In Baptist Training Union and Royal Ambassadors activities he became acquainted with the world-wide missionary work of his denomination. He committed his life to medical missions his first year at nearby Louisiana Polytechnic Institute.

At Louisiana Tech he began dating June Buckner, an old high school friend. They were married his senior year. After he graduated from Louisiana State University School of Medicine and interned at Gorgas Hospital in the Panama Canal Zone, they made formal application for missionary service in the Middle East.

At mid-year of their furlough, Dr. Young was asked if they planned to return to Yemen. "Certainly," he said. "We believe God has called us there and as long as He will permit us to work there, we want to serve."

How does he define his missionary call to the Muslim people of the ancient land of Sheba? "Seeing a need and being able to do something about it is a demonstration of the love of our Savior," he said.

"Our work as Christian missionaries is just beginning in Yemen," he continued. "We hold regular worship services in Arabic in the hospital—the first, so far as we know, to which Yemenis are invited. We want to start a training program for nurses for the hospital. The nurses will also go into the country and promote preventive medicine, treat the sick, and as they are able, bear witness for Christ. And we would like to have an agricultural missionary who can assist Yemeni farmers in increasing crop yields, start programs for growing citrus fruits and olives, and introduce new varieties of chickens. We'd like to assist the Yemenis in every way we can."

6.

Nurse of Zambia

PHYLLIS SPAHR, R.N.

Phyllis Spahr was in Bible college in Philadelphia when the dull and dowdy woman missionary came to Student Missions Fellowship. Phyllis saw her first in the hall. She was wearing a bulky tweed suit that needed pressing, and the heels of her shoes were run down. Committed to a missionary career herself, Phyllis whispered to a girl friend, "I wouldn't want to go out under her board."

Now, after a dozen years in Zambia under the Africa Evangelical Fellowship, Phyllis is certainly not the frumpy, color-me-gray type of single missionary stereotyped in so many novels and movies. Stylish and statuesque, with wavy silvery hair and a college girl's complexion, she is vivacious and warm, exuding a genuine sincerity when she talks about her work as a missionary nurse and teacher. She is much too busy and involved to mope over what might have been had she stayed home and become perhaps a suburban matron hosting teas for the country club set.

Though she has crept past forty and is serving with a mission that includes thirty-six single girls in Zambia alone, and that has only two bachelors among its total membership, Phyllis is not about to don her martyr's cloak. The warmth and vibrance of her voice betrays a sense of accomplishment as she talks about a fulfillment found in helping Zambian girls become missionary nurses to their own people. "There are places on the mission field which single girls can fill better than missionary wives and mothers," she says simply. "I don't think the hospitals would run well without single missionary nurses."

Phyllis directs the nurses training school at the Africa Evangelical Fellowship's 150-bed Muskinge Hospital, one of four hospitals which AEF operates in Southern Africa. All but one of AEF's 285 overseas missionaries (with U.S. headquarters in Glen Ridge, New Jersey) are in southern Africa. The largest field is Zambia, where seventy-one AEF members serve.

Known as Northern Rhodesia until its independence in 1964, kidney-shaped Zambia is slightly larger than Texas. It has four million people among over ninety tribes that speak some seventy-five languages. Literacy among the school-age and adult population stands at 41 percent, unusually high in Africa, thanks to an education-minded British colonial government, missionary efforts dating to David Livingstone (his heart is buried in northern Zambia), and President Kenneth Kaunda's dynamic leadership. Almost half of the people profess Christianity, and the Bible is required learning in public schools.

President Kaunda is the son of a famous Zambian Christian evangelist. He and most members of his government were educated in mission schools. Called a "cool man in a hot spot," Kaunda recently nationalized the foreign-owned copper mines (only the United States produces more copper) and continues efforts to weld the multi-tribal nation into a politically stable and economically prosperous beacon of hope to other African countries.

The Africa Evangelical Fellowship is the largest Protestant mission in Zambia and the second oldest (founded in 1910). The Mission's three-pronged thrust is in evangelism, education, and medicine.

"I can appreciate education," Phyllis says, "though I'm low man on the totem pole in my family." She is comparing herself to her two brothers, one a high school principal with a Ph.D., the other a coach with a master's degree. In addition to nurses' training Phyllis herself has degrees from the University of Pennsylvania and Philadelphia College of Bible (where her father is an accountant). After completing nurses' training at Philadelphia General Hospital she took day classes at the university and studied evenings at the Bible college. "This was really too much in too short a time," she now admits, "although I would advise a girl preparing for missionary nursing to get some Bible training."

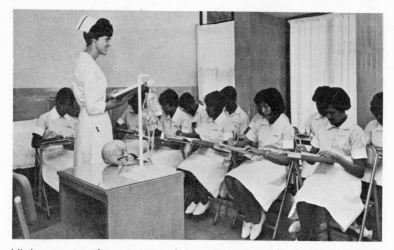

Missionary nurses play a strategic role in training national nurses. Here R.N. Miss Paula Portkamp instructs anatomy class at Baptist Hospital in Guadalajara, Mexico. (Southern Baptist Foreign Mission Board photo)

Besides directing the Muskinge Hospital's nursing school, Phyllis helps the missionary medical staff as needed. "We have two doctors and seven nurses," she explains. "Usually two or three of us are on furlough at any given time. Because I had trained at a big regimented kind of hospital, the informality bothered me a bit at first. But now I like working on a first-name basis. We nurses have much more responsibility than in the United States. We draw blood and start intravenous feeding. We diagnose and treat in some situations. We even order narcotics. Our doctors trust us and back us up. Our staff is really like a family, especially when there's a crisis. When the wife of one of the doctors came down with sleeping sickness from the tsetse fly and her fever went to 106°, we really held on to the Lord and were knit together in a close group."

Phyllis feels that on one count especially her training and work at Philadelphia General Hospital prepared her for Africa. "Most of the patients there and many of the staff were black, so I was adjusted to working with people of another race before coming to Zambia. However, I think the resemblance between African and American blacks does not go much beyond color. American blacks are much closer in culture to American whites than they are to Africans."

Phyllis has thirty-five student nurses. Half of these girls she describes as being "right out of the bush. With them we must start from scratch. We give many of them English names and teach them both English and the local tribal language. A part of the government's detribalization program is to make English the common language.

"The girls are on probation for the first three months, during which time any whom we feel can't make the grade may be asked to return home. The two-year course is actually more like training for practical nurses in the United States.

"I've had to learn patience and let the girls learn to do things for themselves. It's frustrating to stand and watch one try a dozen times to tuck bed sheet corners properly when I could do it right the first time. But I know a nurse must learn how to perform hospital duties in efficient, orderly, and disciplined ways. A poorly tucked in sheet may not harm a patient, but sloppy medical treatment could imperil his life.

"It takes time to erase some of the erroneous impressions which the girls have. Many come to us not even knowing how children are conceived. One girl dashed off her liaison with the remark, 'I was only with the man once, so I know I won't get pregnant.'

"The girls think all Americans are millionaires and, yes, they hear about racial troubles in the U.S. This and the desire to reverse the old system where the Europeans were the bosses sometimes causes problems. One girl flared up at me and complained, 'You're always telling me what to do just because your face is white and mine is black.' 'That isn't it,' I replied. 'I want you to become a good nurse. We all have to answer to somebody else and in the end we have to answer to God.' She calmed down and I think finally reached the point where she didn't resent me."

And Phyllis notes that some of the students wonder why American missionaries come to Africa. "This question," she says, "provides us the chance to explain to them how important Christ is to us and that we want them to experience His love. Many of the girls are from Christian backgrounds but do not know Christ in a personal way. I try to explain that each girl must believe for herself.

"I remember one girl named Sylvia who had been taught by missionaries. We thought she was a Christian. But one Sunday night after I spoke in vesper services, she came to me in tears, saying, 'I want to believe.' I was able to help her come to a decision."

Phyllis recalls that the highlight of the last nurses' school came when President Kaunda visited the hospital. "After the students sang 'The Lord Is My Shepherd' for him, he said, 'The Lord is my Shepherd, too. I hope you will always go to Him with your problems.' We already knew about his strong Christian stand, but hearing his testimony in person encouraged us all."

Another memorable time came when she bandaged some minor wounds for a member of the Zambian Parliament who had been in an auto accident—"My seventh," he told Phyllis with a sheepish grin. She replied, "I've only been in one and suffered a broken back. I've since felt the Lord spared my life for a special reason.

"A look of sadness crossed his face," Phyllis recollects. "He said, 'I used to teach and preach at a mission station before getting into politics. But politics and religion don't mix.' I told him I had never been in politics but did believe that being right with the Lord was more important than anything else."

In remembering such incidents, Phyllis adds, "I don't want to create a false impression that medical missionaries see spectacular results. People just aren't converted every day." She lifts her head and smiles. "You know that bothered me when I came home for my first furlough. I felt guilty because I couldn't say I had won a lot of Africans to Christ. Then someone pointed out to me that we are a team. As Paul says, some plant, some water, but it is God who gives the increase. We work together to bring people to the Lord.

"Right now we especially need some more nurses on our team. We need someone to help with preventive medicine and nutrition. We immunize newborns and hope the mothers will bring them back for their follow-up shots. But many don't. A couple of nurses could take a mobile unit out to the villages and hold baby clinics and teach the mothers nutrition. Then we need someone to be a house mother to the student nurses, counsel them during off times, answer questions, help them with personal problems."

She stops abruptly. "I could go on. I guess I'm trying to say that more missionary nurses are desperately needed. I just wish I could be five people, no—make that ten."

7.

"Dr. Nelson, I Presume"

CLIFTON NELSON, M.D.

One hundred years ago the *New York Herald*'s intrepid Henry Stanley caught sight of a bearded English missionary doctor on the eastern shores of Lake Tanganyika and shouted the now famous salutation, "Dr. Livingstone, I presume."

Livingstone refused to return to England. Six weeks before he died, he wrote, "Nothing will make me give up my work in despair. I encourage myself in the Lord my God and go forward." After his servant found him dead on his knees, grieving African friends removed his heart and buried it beneath a mvula tree. Then they sent his dried, bark-covered body on to England for burial in Westminster Abbey. Tributes from the small and great poured in upon his family. Florence Nightingale wrote his sister, "He has opened those countries for God to enter in. He struck the first blow to abolish a hideous slave trade."

The slave trade has long since been abolished, and hundreds of young men and women have been inspired by Livingstone's plea to "direct your attention to Africa . . . and carry out the work which I have begun." Dr. Clifton Nelson, a stocky Canadian surgeon with curly brown hair, is one. And he serves only two hundred miles east of the village on Lake Tanganyika where Stanley found Livingstone.

As a grammar school boy, young Cliff Nelson pored over biographies of Livingstone and other missionary heroes of the past. He heard living missionaries speak at the Swedish Covenant church in central Alberta, Canada, which he attended with his parents, three brothers, and a sister. One evening after devotions, he whispered to his mother, "I think God may be calling me to be a medical missionary."

The devout farm woman listened quietly while the boy poured out his feelings. "He may well be," she finally said, "but let's make this our secret until you finish high school. Your dad might worry too much about the expense of putting you through medical school."

The next year Cliff started to high school, twenty-six miles across the wheat fields. Lacking transportation, he and an older brother, Roland, batched in a rented apartment, coming home every second weekend. By the time Cliff graduated at sixteen, his father was insisting that he take a pre-med course at the University of Alberta.

But in 1946 Cliff had to step aside for the crowd of older veterans returning from World War II. "Come back next year," the registrar told him.

He found a $5-a-day job tutoring correspondence students in a rural schoolhouse in the remote, frigid Peace River country. He lived alone in a small hut. On winter nights when snow was piled around the hut and the temperature was far below zero, he read his Bible and his missionary biographies and dreamed of the day when he could fulfill Christ's command to "heal the sick."

At the University he more than made up for the lost year of school by qualifying for medical school in two years instead of the usual four. Halfway through medical school he sandwiched in a year's study for a master's degree in physiology, after which he lived and worked in a hospital to help pay expenses for his third and fourth years of med school. Next came a year's internship and another year's surgical residency. "After all this," a young doctor friend asked him, "do you still intend to be a medical missionary?"

Dr. Cliff grinned back. "Certainly. I never lost sight of my goal, thanks to Inter-Varsity Christian Fellowship."

Now he felt ready for marriage to his brunette high school sweetheart, home economist Beth Minogue, daughter of missionaries to Ecuador.

The newlyweds came to Chicago while searching for a mission board sponsor. A Christian doctor friend suggested Cliff "might want to practice a year or two while getting set to go." "No, thanks," Dr. Cliff said in dogged determination. "I've seen too

many doctors who started out to be medical missionaries but
are still in practice here after ten or fifteen years. I want to get
away before I cool off."

While in Chicago where Cliff was taking specialized training
in internal medicine, the Nelsons heard about "Her Majesty's
Overseas Civil Service" which needed Commonwealth nationals
to staff British hospitals in Africa. Their Canadian citizenship
made them eligible and Dr. Nelson saw this as "an opportunity
to see how government was meeting medical needs in a developing country while we continued to look for the right mission
board."

In March 1958, when they arrived in Uganda, the doctor in
charge immediately asked Dr. Nelson if he would like to come
along on a patient visit.

The hospital of 120 beds had two long wards, one male and
one female. Three mud shacks comprised the maternity section.
Four mud shacks housed tuberculars.

An African carrying a hurricane lantern led the two doctors
through the wards, with Dr. Nelson stumbling over people sleeping in the aisles and around beds. "Some of the overflow are
patients," his superior explained. "The rest are family members
whom we allow to sleep near patients." By the time they found
the Britisher's patient, a sick child, Dr. Nelson was thinking,
"How can I practice medicine under circumstances like this?"

"You have increased our doctor staff 25 percent," the Britisher said cheerily. "We had another doctor, an African, but he
left for another assignment just before you arrived. Oh, don't
look so dismayed. We have three nurses to help us."

The next day the medical doctor told Dr. Nelson, "You're in
charge of all surgery and maternity. The opportunities are limit-
less."

The hospital had no electricity, x-ray, or power plant. "I've
got to find my sea legs fast," Dr. Nelson told his wife.

Throughout his student career, he had sought to "look at the
opportunities instead of the problems." Now in Uganda the same
philosophy gained him a sense of balance.

He quickly learned to improvise. A bag of carpentry tools
came in handy. Vise-grip pliers were helpful in setting broken
or fractured bones. A drill could prepare a hole for inserting a
pin for traction. Boards and sometimes even magazines made
splints when nothing better was available.

He soon learned that the hardy Africans had an amazing built-in reserve for snapping back. One man who had been shot in the abdomen with a hunting arrow came in at 4 A.M. When friends had pulled the arrow out, the barbs had raked numerous holes in the intestines. A check showed no blood pressure and the man was given multiple blood transfusions. At eight Dr. Nelson opened him up and sutured three large holes in the stomach and eleven small ones in the bowels. "I don't think he'll make it," he told an assisting doctor. But three weeks later the African walked out of the hospital.

Besides hospital work, Dr. Nelson and his British colleagues did autopsies on all the murder cases in the district. They checked the health of prisoners and food in the local jail. And it was Dr. Nelson's specific responsibility to watch the flogging of juvenile delinquents and make sure the flogger did not go beyond the law.

There were plenty of opportunities to do missionary work. Dr. Nelson shared his faith with patients and staff and various British civil service people in the district. He found many of the Britishers to be dedicated Christians.

The Nelsons got acquainted with Drs. Ted and Peter Williams, two brothers who served at a nearby hospital belonging to the African Inland Mission, a faith missionary society with over seven hundred missionaries in Africa. Shortly before Dr. Nelson's civil service contract was up, he and his wife joined AIM. Following a short furlough trip home to Canada during which their second child was born, they were assigned to AIM's 230-bed Kola Ndoto Hospital in newly independent Tanganyika.

Kola Ndoto Hospital was near a diamond mine in a thickly populated jungle area between two fabled lakes: Lake Victoria to the north, the size of Scotland and the second largest fresh water lake in the world, and Lake Tanganyika, the longest inland lake in the world.

Only the year before, Tanganyika, located next to Uganda in the heart of East Africa and one third larger than Texas, had gained independence from Britain under the leadership of Jules Nyerere. A year after their arrival, Tanganyika federated with the island nation of Zanzibar to form the United Republic of Tanzania under a proclaimed policy of democratic socialism.

A product of Catholic mission schools, President Nyerere had been the first Tanganyikan to graduate from a British university. A fourth of his twelve million people were Christians, mostly Catholics and Lutherans, but with a large membership in the

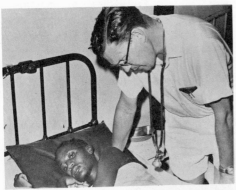

As a farm boy in Alberta,
Canada, Cliff Nelson devoured
biographies of Dr. David
Livingstone. Now he serves
the Africa Inland Mission
not far from where the great
Dr. Livingstone was buried.
(MAP photo)

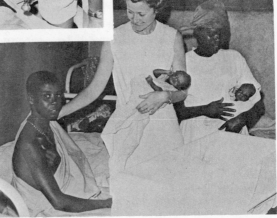

Dr. Ruth King Dix has just delivered these pygmy twins at Dr.
Carl Becker's Africa Inland Mission hospital in the Congo.
(MAP photo)

Africa Inland Church founded by the Africa Inland Mission, which had fifty-six missionaries in the country.* About 30 percent of the population were Muslims and 40 percent adhered to the 123 tribal religions in the country.

The Nelsons were quickly fascinated by their newly adopted country. Centuries before Christ Tanganyika had carried on trade with Arabia, Persia, and China. A fantastic array of wildlife swarmed across the mainland plateau and up the slopes of Mount Kilimanjaro, Africa's highest peak at 19,340 feet. Naturalists had identified over a thousand species of birds and over a hundred varieties of snakes in the area. Largely agriculturist in economy, mainland Tanzania was the world's largest producer of sisal, used for making rope, with the island of Zanzibar the greatest world source for clove.

But only 12 percent of the population was counted literate because of the numerous unwritten tribal languages, and there was only one doctor for every twenty-five thousand persons. In the western area surrounding Kola Ndoto Hospital, the doctor-population ratio was worse, one to eighty thousand.

Members of the Sukuma tribe (one and a quarter million population and largest in the country) said that health conditions had been much worse before the coming of "our angel of light." They referred to Dr. Nina Maynard, who, with her general missionary husband, had founded the hospital. Dr. Nina was dead, but her husband, William, past ninety, and his second wife occupied a house next door to the Nelsons. The Africans revered the old man, but were not so worshipful of younger missionaries. Dr. Nelson realized that in this time of nationalistic fervor whites, even missionaries, had to earn the respect of the Africans.

In 1964 the Mission responded to the rising demand for Africans to take charge of institutions by placing several of its ten hospitals in four African countries under the African Inland Church. The African Church asked Dr. Nelson to continue as medical director of the Kola Ndoto Hospital with a Tanzanian national as business manager. The remaining missionary staff then consisted of AIM's Dr. Jeanne Shaw and two nurses.

The takeover by African church leaders applied to the properties of other missions as well. Several missionaries left the country because they thought their new bosses too haughty and

---

*Tanzania is now the largest Lutheran mission field in the world with 212 missionaries.

overbearing. But Dr. Nelson's response was, "I'm ready to step down and be just a staff doctor whenever a qualified African doctor is ready to be medical director."

With four children, Beth Nelson still found time to teach and counsel Tanzanian women. Her doctor husband had what a visiting specialist from the United States called "an impossible job." Besides administrative responsibilities, he and Dr. Shaw handled about 1,400 operations yearly, 350 of them major. Fortunately, they had the assistance of a trained corps of Tanzanian nurses, graduates of the hospital's nursing school. And the hospital benefited from x-ray equipment, running water, electric lights, and a well-run laboratory.

There were always more patient needs than available time. Deciding whom to treat first required the wisdom of Solomon. Usually, this meant taking first those who could be helped the most with the least resources, then next those who could be improved moderately with a moderate amount of care. Last came those who could be helped very little with even the expenditure of major resources. A child near death with malaria, for example, that could be brought back from the brink very quickly would be treated ahead of an old man suffering from a variety of chronic diseases.

In staff prayer meetings, missionaries and Africans prayed together for wisdom and compassion. "We can learn to say 'no' with love to relatives of a patient whose condition is hopeless," Dr. Nelson stressed. "We can show the love of Christ by the way we walk through a ward and look at patients."

Fortunately, the hospital had additional help from visiting specialists. From the diamond mine close by, two doctors specializing in heart problems and orthopedics stopped past once each week. A Christian eye surgeon in private practice from Nairobi, Kenya, came for two days every two months. A government tuberculosis specialist helped a day or more each month. And short-term doctors from abroad arrived periodically to give from a day to two weeks to the patients.

A visiting U.S. neurologist was especially impressed by the devotion of the staff. "Cliff, I can't understand you," he said. "Your staff is so overworked. You all seem to enjoy it and get along well with one another."

Dr. Nelson smiled back as he replied, "What you see is Christ in us giving us joy and strength to serve."

In 1968 the Nelsons came home for an eight-month furlough.

Dr. Nelson's blue eyes fairly sparkled as he talked with me about his work. "I'm convinced," he said, "that Christian doctors in the United States and Canada aren't aware of the opportunities, tremendous excitement, and rewards in medical missions. They look too much at the negative aspects—the lack of equipment, for example. I tell them, 'Think of what you can do for the scores of critically ill patients. Like the woman in labor for two days who arrives at the hospital at 3:00 A.M. after bouncing over seventy-five miles of rough road in a Land Rover. How exciting to maybe do a caesarean section in the next hour, perhaps save her life, and present her with a beautiful baby. In that short time you can change her whole outlook on life and open her up to the gospel for the first time.'

"And I say, 'Think of your witness to the student nurses and African staff members. We've seen Muslim nurses affected by the Christlike life they see in African Christians and missionaries. Two have accepted Christ. How exciting to open your office and home to these young Africans and share the reason for your service with them.' "

Later he told a convention of medical missionaries, "Nationalism is a world-wide phenomenon of the mid-twentieth century. We must see it not as a problem, but as an opportunity to let nationals have the center stage, while we man the wings, giving encouragement and support. They will win more of their own people through the ministry of healing than we will."

After the doctor had spoken, a convention leader summed up his impressions. And he gave a sense of direction for the whole audience when he said, "The day of missionaries like Cliff Nelson is just beginning."

8.

Sacred Agent HI8XHS

HOWARD SHOEMAKE

The shirt-sleeved, dark-haired ex-president of the Dominican Republic leaned across the coffee table in his Miami exile home and spoke intensely. "Howard Shoemake is such a good man for my poor country," he said. "He was the first Protestant minister I ever knew. He came to see me about the medical aid program. He prayed with me. I ordered the departments of government to give him all the help needed. He saved the lives of thousands of our babies."

Donald Reid Cabral had been ousted by a military junta during the 1965 Dominican revolution which had attracted worldwide attention because of U.S. intervention. "Now there will be progress," he told me, "but if we had twenty more men like Howard Shoemake, there would be more progress."

I found other on-the-scene observers during the Dominican revolution equally as lavish in their praise of Howard Shoemake's service. Malcolm McClean, U.S. Public Affairs officer: "Howard isn't the kind to stay away from danger when he knows he's needed. He ran a one-man rescue squad during the revolution. Concern is the word for him." George Brown, staff assistant to Ambassador W. Tapley Bennett, Jr.: "Howard's credentials as a Good Samaritan were recognized by everybody. In my view he more than carried out a missionary's role in the Dominican Republic." The wife of a prominent Santo Domingo businessman: "A wonderful man, that Meester Shoemake. Is the best embassy the United States has in our country. He knows no poor, no rich, no ugly, no pretty, no religion. He's helping for everybody."

I went to see for myself. What I learned about Howard Shoemake's revolutionary ministry convinced me that he—an evangelical missionary—is the most influential foreigner in the
troubled little country that Columbus "loved most."

At the Santo Domingo airport I picked Shoemake out of the
crowd instantly. Six-four, 240 pounds, a strong full face shaded
by wavy locks of dark hair flecked by gray, he stood in sharp
contrast to the diminutive, small-faced Dominicans. At home I
met Dorothy Dell Shoemake, a tall, slim woman who moved with
the grace of a southern belle, the Shoemakes' two young sons,
and a daughter in pigtails. Two older sons were in the United
States.

Over coffee Howard sketched his missionary career. First a
Texas pastor for ten years ("the go-go-go type," he explained),
then a "conventional church-building" Southern Baptist missionary in Colombia and Ecuador for thirteen years, Shoemake had
asked his board for a new country "where the trees weren't cut
and the stumps hadn't been pulled." The Southern Baptist board
sent him to the Dominican Republic in 1962 shortly after the
assassination of long-time despot Rafael Trujillo, sometimes
called "the Hitler of the Caribbean." " 'Our country is like a
poor child that has lost a bad father and doesn't know what to
do,' a Dominican told me when I arrived," Shoemake recalled.

The airline lost his baggage, forcing Shoemake to stay near,
close to his Santo Domingo hotel. "Being short, Dominicans had
no clothes for an elephant," he explained.

The lost baggage that kept him from touring the countryside
proved to be a blessing in disguise. He used the time in the
capital to gather some striking statistics:

Economy. Unemployment over 35 percent. Economy drained
by fleeing Trujillo family, rumored to have escaped with a half
billion dollars. Wages, 20–35¢ an hour. Prices on hard goods
higher than in U.S.

Education. Fifty percent of adult population illiterate; only
25 percent of school-age population in school; less than 1 percent
finishing high school.

Health. Only 63 percent of urban population receiving water
service. Infant mortality 135 per 1000 first year—more than
three times the rate of U.S. slums. Only 80 registered nurses
for 11,400 beds to serve 3.5 million people. Many beds empty
because of inadequate hospital financing.

Religion. Over 90 percent "baptized" Catholic. A dozen Protestant groups majoring on education and church building, tolerated but with little influence.

Politics. Uncertain, with twenty-six political parties struggling to fill the power vacuum left by the Trujillo regime. Communist agitation, principally from Radio Havana.

Shoemake reported back to his board which voted to place his family as permanent missionaries in the Dominican Republic. Shortly before departure he was given a ham radio set. At the same time he had an unusual spiritual experience. "One morning I awoke about 4:30 and began reading Isaiah. God seemed to be giving me a message historically addressed to Cyrus. Several phrases stood out like neon lights: 'I will loose the loins of kings . . . I will go before thee, and make the crooked places straight . . .' (Isa. 45:1-2). It was as if God were saying, 'Howard, I will let you witness to presidents and cabinet ministers if you will let Me direct your steps.' "

The ham set got Shoemake into the National Radio Club, which elected him a director and asked him to help draw up a new constitution. Club friendship with an employee of the government television network resulted in free regular telecasting of the Baptist TV dramatic series, *This Is the Answer!*—the first religious broadcast ever on the Santo Domingo station.

Instead of sending them away or teaching them at home, the Shoemakes enrolled their children in the private Carol Morgan School, jointly supported by the foreign colony and Dominican parents. Howard was first elected an alternate member, then president of the school board.

When Hurricane Edith struck on the heels of a bloodless government coup, Shoemake helped in rescue operations, then devised a new civil defense plan for the entire country.

In 1964, eighteen months after arrival, Shoemake finally began Baptist services in a rented club building, once used as a gambling casino. By this time he was so well known for his Good Samaritanship that the first services were televised for the Santo Domingo news. When a visiting Christian Medical Society team from the U.S. needed an evangelical leader to take on a survey, he was the natural choice. Accompanied by the Dominican minister of health, the team toured the countryside and saw appalling medical needs, especially among babies stricken with gastroenteritis. Again and again, Dr. C. Everett Koop pointed to feverish, dehydrating babies and said, "That little one will be dead within forty-eight hours if something isn't done." The health minister noted grimly that 60 percent of all deaths the previous year had been among children below five—half resulting from gastroenteritis. In obvious anguish, Shoemake moaned, "If we can't help these babies, I think I'll die."

Back in Santo Domingo the team members compared notes and decided that poor hygiene, flies, hot weather, and improper food care helped pave the way for infection with the dysentery bacillus or with an organism such as streptococcus. The onslaught of deadly gastroenteritis followed: fever, irritability, vomiting, diarrhea, telltale slaty gray skin showing rapid dehydration, parched mucous membranes, then stupor or convulsions. Unless there was rehydration with suitable body fluids such as 5 percent glucose solution, death within twenty-four hours was almost certain.

When asked about the availability of facilities and fluids for rehydration in his country, the health minister solemnly shook his head. "Only one hospital in Santo Domingo can help and only on a limited basis," he said.

The obstacles appeared formidable. Government health education was inadequate and incomprehensible to the mothers. Impure water and poor sanitation made it easy for children, especially babies, to become infected. Most doctors were in the large cities, and few of these had either sufficient knowledge or medical equipment to treat gastroenteritis. With only eighty registered nurses in the country, hospital patient care was largely handled by inadequately trained practical nurses.

The team agreed that the biggest need was public health education. Shoemake and the minister of health engineered a unique nursing school in Santiago, the country's second city. The Free Methodist mission provided two missionary nurse instructors. Two local doctors volunteered to teach part time. The local Catholic university furnished buildings and labs. Local hospitals took in student nurses for on-the-job training.

The minister of health promised to have health manuals simplified and distributed. But there still remained the urgent need to save the thousands of children who would certainly die before the preventive programs could take effect.

Raymond Knighton, then executive director of CMS, said, "Through our Medical Assistance Programs (MAP) we can provide fluids and scalp-vein kits for intravenous insertion of the fluids into dehydrating babies. We can also send short-term doc-

tors and medical students to train Dominican personnel to use
the kits in rehydration units set up within hospitals throughout
the country."

After the Dominican president and minister of health welcomed this program, Knighton asked Shoemake to be the on-the-
scene director.

"But I've got more work to do now than I can handle,"
Shoemake protested.

"What can be more important than saving the lives of babies?"
Knighton retorted.

The Texan had no answer.

He used a room in his home for the MAP office, hired the
girl next door as secretary, and stored medical supplies in the
rented church building. Julian Cannon, a blind ham operator in
Chicago, agreed to set up phone patches between Shoemake and
Knighton after the latter returned home.

The first crates of fluids, scalp-vein kits, and other necessary
equipment arrived. A team of nine U.S. doctors and four medical
students followed the medicine.

Under Howard Shoemake's supervision, the short-term team
equipped the first center—two rooms in the Puello Hospital in
Santo Domingo. The program for this first dedication set the
pattern for ceremonies at eleven other centers located strategi-
cally throughout the country: a luncheon, recognition of special
guests, a devotional talk by one of the visiting Christian doctors,
a short talk by a government official, and a prayer of dedication.

President Donald Reid Cabral was scheduled to speak at the
first dedication. When Shoemake arrived the seats at the head
table were filled. But an official saw him and escorted him to a
seat beside the president.

After each dedication the MAP medical team remained for
a few days to train local personnel before moving to the next
hospital. Within three months MAP units were operating in
twelve hospitals and the Dominican health ministry had an equal
number going. Some units averaged forty to forty-five scalp-vein
infusions each day.

When administered by trained hands, each life-saving infusion
was amazingly simple. With the baby held in position by the
mother, the scalp was cleansed with an antiseptic; the needle
point pierced the vein at an oblique angle and the force of
gravity sent the precious fluid into the bloodstream. The rate of
flow had to be carefully regulated, because too much too fast

could balloon the infant's veins and cause them to rupture. Then the nurse or doctor placed a piece of cotton or gauze beneath the hub of the needle and anchored it in an immobile angle of about 30 degrees with adhesive tape. With the flow regulated, the infant could be cared for by its mother until the infusion was completed.

Dominican newspapers headlined the program for saving thousands of lives, identifying Director Shoemake as an evangelical missionary. Shoemake began receiving calls from "evangelical" doctors. Before he had not known any even existed.

He organized about twenty doctors into the first overseas chapter of the Christian Medical Society and began monthly round tables in his home. The evangelical doctors invited their colleagues to the round tables where a Christian doctor gave a short devotion, followed by lecture and discussion on a current medical problem.

Shoemake himself brought a doctor who had attended a few services in his church. By birth a Catholic, Dr. Agustin Cornelio had been reading a Bible given to him by an evangelical doctor several years before. After the discussion, Shoemake suggested they close with short prayers. When the doctor next to Dr. Cornelio finished, Howard opened his mouth to pray. Suddenly Dr. Cornelio began a halting but fervent petition.

The following week Shoemake met Dra.* Josefina Roman, a young gynecologist who also taught at the University of Santo Domingo Medical School. She wanted to know more about the Bible and how to become a Christian. In time she became his second doctor convert.

Dra. Gladys Germosen de Mieses he met in a tuberculosis hospital. She came to the round table, attended Shoemake's services, and professed faith in Christ.

His fourth doctor convert was Dra. Gisela Cucurullo whom he met after the dedication of a rehydration center. She and her doctor husband had been watching *This Is the Answer!* on television. Dra. Cucurullo came to Shoemake's church and along with her daughters accepted Christ. Her husband, director of Planned Parenthood in Santo Domingo, declared himself "most sympathetic" with evangelical beliefs.

Three weeks after the last MAP rehydration center was dedicated in April 1965, the nation erupted into bloody civil war. Downtown Santo Domingo became a battleground as U.S. Ma-

*Women doctors are "Doctora" (Dra.) in Spanish.

rines marched in to "protect" U.S. citizens and "keep Communists from taking over." Howard Shoemake accompanied his family to Puerto Rico on an evacuation ship, then returned at the special request of the U.S. ambassador.

Rebels calling themselves "Constitutionalists" and backed by an undetermined number of Communists seized a large area of the old section of Santo Domingo in which Shoemake's church was located. "Loyalists" held the newer section. Troops from other Latin American countries under the banner of the Organization of American States moved in and established an international free zone between the warring camps.

Shoemake's home was near the neutral zone, and political refugees of various stripes began flocking there. The Dominican Red Cross asked him to distribute badly needed medical supplies about the city.

The need for dextrose fluids for intravenous feeding was especially critical. Shoemake was driving towards his church to get several jars stored there when he was stopped by rebel soldiers. "We can't let you take medicines out to aid those who are fighting against us," an officer said. "Not even if they are in your church. Besides, some of our defenders are on the second floor."

Shoemake explained that he was working with the Red Cross and wanted to help suffering people in all zones. He added, "If I can't take medicines out of your territory, I can't bring them in."

The rebel officer relented. "We will trust you. Get your medicines."

Shoemake not only got the medicines directly from underneath the nest of rebels but also got a free pass from the rebel leadership. "You're the only man besides the papal nuncio and the Peace Corps director who has permission to drive everywhere in the city," the Red Cross director told him.

With the sound of gunfire in the distance, Shoemake radioed Ray Knighton in Wheaton, Illinois. "We're running low on dextrose and medicines. What can you send?"

"Anything we've got in our warehouse and can beg from the drug companies," Knighton shot back. "We'll try to get the Navy to fly it down."

Shortly, thirteen tons of fluids and antibiotics were flown into the airport and trucked to Shoemake's house. Within hours the medicines were flowing to every hospital in the beleaguered city.

Though not a doctor, Southern Baptist missionary Rev. Howard Shoemake directs a unique medical ministry in the Dominican Republic. With medicines supplied by Medical Assistance Programs, church-related programs under Shoemake's direction will serve over 240,000 patients this year. Shoemake is shown here ordering medicines by ham radio.

Crowds of patients form outside the MAP clinics in the Dominican Republic to await care by Dominican doctors. Here Dra. Gladys Germosen de Mieses, one of Shoemake's four doctor converts, looks for seriously ill patients. (MAP photo)

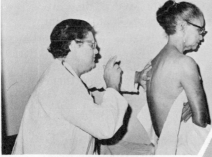

Dra. Germosen de Mieses examines a lady patient. (MAP photo)

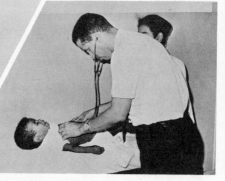

Above: Another of Shoemake's doctor converts, Dr. Agustin Cornelio, checks a small Dominican in a clinic. **Left:** Shoemake believes Dominican Christians must minister to their own people. Two church ladies dispense medicines in a clinic pharmacy. (MAP photos)

One of the many hazardous trips Shoemake made for the Red Cross was to deliver emergency oxygen to an asthmatic child who was near death. The ambulance drivers had refused to go because the cylinders "looked like bombs." Shoemake made the trip unharmed.

Hostilities slackened after several weeks. The rebels who had occupied the second floor above Howard's church left, and he resumed church services. His family returned from Puerto Rico.

Now the city was faced with the threat of an epidemic by disease-carrying rats. Shoemake radioed Knighton who "happened" to have two hundred tons of donated Tri-Ban rat poison overflowing the MAP warehouse. U.S. AID paid the ocean freight and boxes of Tri-Ban were distributed to every household in the capital. Under Shoemake's direction, Santo Domingo had a "Day of the Rats" on which thousands of rodents died.

Both during and after the hostilities, hundreds of anxious people flocked to use Shoemake's ham radio. In one two-month period he made 2,517 phone patches, mostly calls to relatives of U.S. soldiers and others in Santo Domingo. One visitor dubbed him Sacred Agent HI8XHS, after the call letters of his radio.

He handled personally a number of medical emergencies on the ham network. He placed one call to famed heart surgeon Dr. Michael DeBakey in Houston to arrange for an operation on a Dominican friend. He made another to set up transportation to the United States for a six-year-old Dominican girl, daughter of a presidential palace guard, whose lungs were slowly drowning in regurgitated blood. She had been born with a three-chambered instead of the normal four-chambered heart, and needed an artificial heart wall to prevent too much blood from flowing back into the lungs. Shoemake's ham "diplomacy" arranged for a U.S. plane to fly little Ingrid Vargas and her parents to Washington where they were kept overnight by a ham Air Force major, then put on a plane for Oklahoma City and scheduled heart surgery at the Free Methodist Deaconness Hospital. The operation was successful and the family returned to Santo Domingo and began attending a Baptist church.

The Christian Medical Society and Medical Assistance Programs became separate organizations in 1965. Shoemake continued to represent both in Santo Domingo until his new missionary colleagues insisted that he drop one. He resigned from CMS and continued with MAP in addition to pastoring his church and helping his colleagues start new congregations.

But the Dominican evangelical doctors kept after him. They wanted a service ministry with an evangelical witness to needy Dominicans. The only evangelical medical ministry then operating in the country was the nurses' school which Shoemake had helped the Free Methodists and Catholics start in Santiago.

Shoemake consulted with Ray Knighton, who had left CMS to become president of MAP. They proposed a clinic in downtown Santo Domingo where patients could consult Christian doctors and receive free medicines channeled through MAP from U.S. drug companies.

The doctors jumped for the idea. Dr. Cornelio, whose wife had recently died, leaving him with three motherless children, found a second-floor apartment. They moved the stock of medicines from the church building to the new place and curtained off three bedrooms for examining rooms; the living room became the reception area and the kitchen, a pharmacy.

The clinic was open each weekday afternoon. Each patient paid one dollar for the doctor's examination; prescribed medicine was dispensed by lay Christians at no charge. Half of the dollar went to the examining doctor, half to expenses. "We want people to keep their dignity and not be dependent on us," Shoemake insisted.

Liberal social legislation gave every person the right to a doctor's care. Doctors had to give time in government hospitals. But the government had little money for medicine which poor people could not afford to buy from pharmacies. The Christian clinic was a godsend to hundreds of inner-city poor, for here they could have all the medicine they needed.

In July 1966, the Baptist church in the Ozama suburb of Santo Domingo opened a clinic in Sunday school rooms on the pattern of the first. Dr. Cornelio and Dra. Germosen, two of Shoemake's four Dominican doctor converts, served here. A few months later Shoemake's Santo Domingo Baptist Church rented an aged residence in a war-ravaged *barrio* (neighborhood) of northern Santo Domingo. Weekday patients and Sunday worshipers used the same pews in the largest room. Waiting patients listened to recordings of Christian radio programs in Spanish. The first Sunday, forty attended Sunday school.

Other churches quickly got on the medical bandwagon: Pentecostal, Brethren, Free Methodist, and Seventh Day Adventist. A clinic was started in Santiago, two in rural villages where there were no doctors, not even places to buy aspirins.

By January 1971, twenty thousand patients a month were being served at twenty-six Christian clinics, all staffed by Dominican Christian doctors, all dispensing free medicines provided through MAP. Two of Shoemake's four doctor converts, Dr. Cornelio and Dra. Germosen, were giving full time to the clinics. Dra. Roman, another convert, had migrated to the United States. Dra. Cucurullo took care of her family and helped in church activities.

The Rehabilitation Center, the only facility for crippled children in the country, asked Shoemake's help in purchasing needed equipment through MAP. He arranged for a U.S. AID grant of $5,000, and MAP bought the equipment wholesale in the United States. Then Shoemake raised $1,000 from Dominican friends to pay the freight for a year's supply of medicines from MAP to the Rehabilitation Center.

For his revolutionary medical and social work, Howard Shoemake has received numerous honors. He serves as the Protestant member of the Rehabilitation Center's three-man administrative board. He is the only foreigner on the powerful six-member National Board of Directors of Civil Defense. A delegation of nuns presented him with an award on television. The Dominican Navy gave him a medal. And because of the MAP program, MAP's president, Ray Knighton, was given the country's second highest honor—knighthood in the Order of Christopher Columbus.

During my visit to the Dominican Republic I saw the clinics in action. One sticky afternoon I dropped in at the first one where over a hundred patients waited in line for treatment. When Shoemake and I entered the crowded waiting room, Dr. Socrates Perez greeted us. Then he told the waiting patients with a smile, " 'The Giant' is here to give a message from God's Word."

"The Giant," Howard Shoemake, opened his Spanish Testament and read about Christ as the Good Shepherd. Then he prayed earnestly while the patients listened in thoughtful silence.

I next saw Howard Shoemake when he came to Chicago as one of two featured speakers for the semiannual Conference on International Health sponsored by the American Medical Association. The other was Dean Rusk.

I sat in the audience of physicians, many of whom were internationally famous because of their contributions to world health, and listened to "the Giant" from Santo Domingo describe the unique Dominican ministries.

He unashamedly told the distinguished audience, "We don't see healing and preaching as either/ors, but as inseparable companions in our expression of love for the suffering Dominicans."

He described the ministry of the clinics as staffed by Dominicans. "We don't want foreign missionary doctors," he declared, "except for short-term assistance. We want to win more national doctors who will witness for their faith both in what they do and say."

He unveiled plans for the future: "A mobile unit to reach backwoods people who can't come to the cities; public health education programs on FM radio."

When he said his final amen, there was a burst of applause, and the physicians rushed to shake the hand of a revolutionary-minded preacher who had made medicine a vital ministry in the troubled country which Columbus called "the land of God." *

---

*For the expanded story of Howard Shoemake's revolutionary medical service in the Dominican Republic, read the author's *Intrigue in Santo Domingo* (Waco, Texas: Word Books, 1968).

9.

Doctor to the Montagnards

E. ARDEL VIETTI, M.D.

The tanned young missionary pointed to the green jungle rushing up to meet our fast descending C-130. "There's a little hospital down there, surrounded by Viet Cong."

I scanned the rugged terrain until I saw some buildings in a clearing. They looked as if they were being used, although I saw no movement. "That's Dr. Vietti's hospital," Jim Lewis continued. "Americans haven't been there since she and two other missionaries were captured in 1962. But Raday tribal nurses still keep it open."

A few minutes later we were in a jeep with a U.S. AID refugee worker. After a brief stop at the AID office in Ban Me Thuot, he insisted on driving us to the ruins of the Christian and Missionary Alliance compound that had been destroyed barely four months before in the 1968 Tet offensive. We could not, of course, think of visiting Dr. Vietti's leprosarium, eight miles out into the jungle.

We picked our way across the rubble that had been the homes of happy missionary families. We looked at the memorial over the common grave where three of the six missionaries killed during a Tet battle were buried. We viewed the shattered remains of the clinic building where tribal nurses from Dr. Vietti's jungle hospital had received medicines before Tet.

Jim smiled grimly. "We're going to rebuild and continue work from here," he said. "Already our nurses are coming into town for brief visits and bringing medicines for the Radays. Later

when the security is better, we'll go back to the jungle leprosarium. Maybe Dr. Vietti will be released by then. If—" and he
paused, "—she's still alive."

Eleanor Ardel Vietti, M.D., was a missionary physician of
first rank, according to Dr. John Dick, a short-term Mennonite
doctor who helped her perform many operations on leprosy patients. "Ardel was afraid like everyone else," Dr. Dick told me
in his home in Winnipeg, Canada. "But she cared enough to stay
until she was captured."

"If she's still alive—and we keep hoping," missionary nurse
Millie Ade declared, "you can be sure that she's helping the sick,
even if they are Viet Cong."

Ardel Vietti was the daughter of a diamond exporter and oil
geologist. She and her twin sister, Theresa, spent their early
childhood in South America. When the family moved to Houston,
Texas, they entered San Jacinto High School. In the lunch room
one day Ardel noticed two girls bow their heads over their trays.
Typically curious and frank, she walked over to their table and
asked, "Why did you do that?"

Marian Carlson smiled and said, "We were thanking God for
our food."

"Well, I admire you for your spunk," Ardel said. "Not many
kids around here would do that."

Daisy Womack, the other girl, looked at Ardel. "How about
visiting our church? You can learn more about what we believe there. Marian's dad is the pastor."

Ardel smiled. "Give me the address and the time of your
services. Maybe I'll surprise you and come."

The following Sunday Ardel rode her bicycle to the church
on Anita Street. She was welcomed by Marian and Daisy, who
introduced her to other young people. Ardel returned that
evening with her younger brother, Vincent. A few weeks later
she declared her faith in Christ and asked for baptism.

The dark-haired girl became one of the most active youths
in the church. Sometimes her younger brother came with her;
often she came alone on her bike, even after dark. Once after
she was accosted by a man, her church friends offered to give
her a ride. "No, I can take care of myself," Ardel insisted with
a toss of her long pigtails.

While she was still in high school, Ardel committed her life to
medical missions at a church camp. Pastor Carlson told the
congregation, "This stubborn girl will stick."

The Christian and Missionary Alliance camp headquarters was in Arlington, Texas, near Fort Worth. One summer Ardel heard that the camp buildings needed cleaning up in preparation for scheduled activities. She and Vincent arrived two weeks early to surprise the new camp superintendent and his wife, who were dismayed at the work yet to do. "We're here to help," the vivacious girl announced. The two cleaned stoves, washed and stacked dishes, swept floors. The camp was in good order for opening day.

At Rice University, where she was a science major, Ardel led her class. At least one faculty member termed her "a genius." From Rice she and Theresa went on to the University of Texas medical school.

Pursuing her commitment to medical missions, Ardel spent the summer of 1953 with a girl friend combating a deadly measles epidemic among poverty-stricken Chol Indians in southern Mexico. Here she saw how Wycliffe Bible translator John Beekman and his wife, Elaine, were overworked in trying to do both Bible translation and medical work. "Oh, if only I had my medical training over," she told the Wycliffe couple. "There's so much I could do."

While in medical school she participated in the Christian Medical Society. When graduation neared, she wrote the CMS director, then Ray Knighton, asking if he would recommend her to a good hospital for internship. Knighton contacted CMS leader Dr. Howard Hamlin, chief of surgeons at Chicago's South Shore Hospital. Ardel came to Chicago, where she impressed Knighton as being "a young woman who would make a contribution to medical missions."

After a year at South Shore and a residency at Texas General Hospital in Wichita Falls, she applied to the foreign mission board of the Christian and Missionary Alliance. "I know I'm deficient in theology and linguistics," she confessed, "but please let me use my abilities in medical practice somewhere."

She was interviewed and examined in New York. Her weight was borderline. But there was an acute need for a doctor at the new leprosarium the Alliance had built in the central Vietnamese highlands with the aid of the American Leprosy Mission and the Mennonite Central Committee. Board leaders decided to appoint her without delay. The enthusiastic Dr. Vietti began preparing to leave as soon as possible.

The year she left for Asia—1957—Viet Nam was creeping into

the world news. Following the French defeat at Dien Bien Phu
in 1954, the country had been sliced into two states, with almost
a million refugees moving south from the Communist north.
Political skies were darkening as anti-government guerillas who
had fought under Ho Chi Minh against the French began harass-
ing the South Viet Nam countryside. There was much uneasi-
ness among the Montagnard ("mountain people") tribespeople
in the central highlands who lived around the new leprosy hospital. Tribal leaders had long been complaining that the Saigon
government treated them like second-class citizens. Some wanted
an independent nation of their own.

The mission gang welcomed Dr. Ardel to Ban Me Thuot, a
provincial capital in the heart of tiger and elephant country and
hunting center for past Vietnamese emperors and French officers.
Dr. Ardel met the Alliance nurses—Millie Ade, Ruth Wilting,
and blond Olive Kingsbury, whom the Raday tribespeople called
"Sister White"—and she enjoyed fellowship with the "compound
missionaries" who lived in Ban Me Thuot near the Raday Bible
school—Mr. and Mrs. Gordon Smith, the senior missionaries, the
Robert Ziemer family, life-of-the-party single girl Carolyn Griswold, and other missionaries.

The leprosarium buildings nestled in a verdant valley eight
miles out of the city on a hundred and fifty acres of land. The
U-shaped "sick" hospital was the largest building and contained
the surgery rooms and ward beds for about thirty patients. The
"well" hospital for thirty more able patients was a few hundred
feet away. Other buildings scattered about the grounds included
missionary residences and a chapel where daily services for
"well" patients were held. Services for "sick" patients were held
inside the main hospital. One small residence had been reserved
for the new doctor.

Before her arrival, Ardel had spent several weeks observing
and studying at the Seventh Day Adventist Hospital in Chiang
Mai, Thailand. There she added to her understanding of the
basic facts that she already knew about the disease that affects
an estimated ten to fifteen million people in Africa, Asia, and
South America, and some scattered sufferers in highly developed
countries, including the United States.

Leprosy, or Hansen's disease (so named for the Norwegian
physician who first demonstrated the presence of the rod-shaped
bacterium called *Mycobacterium leprae*), is caused by infectious
bacilli invading the skin and attacking first the tiny nerve end-

ings, then larger nerve trunks. Ardel was aware that the first sign of the disease was the appearance of a spot or a variety of spots, insensitive to pain, on any part of the body. While not damaging the brain or central nervous system, the leprosy bacilli could affect nerves supplying power to muscles, resulting in muscle paralysis. Damage to sensory nerves might result in loss of sensation or anesthesia in the body member or area supplied by the nerve. Thus, unable to feel pain or sensations of touch in affected areas, the patient was easily susceptible to severe burns, cuts and bruises, and wound infections. A tragic sequence of events often followed as fingers, toes, hands, and feet were simply worn away by constant unconscious use. Dr. Ardel realized that much of this crippling and deformity could be prevented by early medical treatment and by educating the patient to avoid injury to anesthetized areas.

At the jungle leprosarium she also became keenly aware of inhumane discrimination. The poor Radays, about three hundred thousand in number and the largest of some thirty minority groups in South Viet Nam, had been considered mere beasts of burden by the haughty French. One French colonial official had told an Alliance missionary, "We don't care about the Montagnards. They're good for building roads. That's all." Many Vietnamese officials who had taken over from the French had much the same attitude. But the Alliance missionaries who had first come to Viet Nam back in 1911 believed in the inherent worth of the tribespeople and had begun an ambitious work of evangelism and Bible translation in the tribal languages. When Dr. Ardel arrived, Bob Ziemer was hard at work on the Raday New Testament, and other Alliance translators were making progress in three other tribal languages.

But the plight of the tribal leprosy sufferers was infinitely worse. As soon as the disease became apparent, ignorant tribespeople, fearful of infection, took drastic action. In some villages a leper would be herded into a hut and the building set afire. In others the victim would be driven into the jungle. The only hope of the poor leprosy sufferers was the mission hospital near Ban Me Thuot.

Meeting the acute need called for two lines of attack: Treat and rehabilitate advanced cases at the leprosarium. Identify and treat others who were infected with the bacilli but did not yet show visual symptoms or signs of leprosy.

As news spread through the surrounding area that a doctor

was at the newly built leprosarium, pitiful victims began straggling onto the grounds. Some hobbled in pain. Some stumped along on mutilated feet. No one in need was turned away, not even when patients had to sleep on the floor.

Surgery had to be performed on many victims. Dr. Ardel, assisted by trained Raday nurses and missionary nurses, did many below-the-knee amputations as a last resort. When possible, she did corrective surgery that restored normal function to limbs of patients who had been crippled by the disease. The new sulfone drug, Dapsone, and other remedies were administered regularly to patients. No attempt was made to isolate patients from their families who frequently accompanied them to the leprosarium.*

Patients with anesthetic hands or feet were educated to be on constant guard against possible injury. They learned to be careful about handling hot cooking pots and burning logs, to inspect their hands and feet daily for injuries, and to examine and care for their eyes. Habitually frank, Dr. Ardel could even be gruff with patients who repeatedly failed to follow instructions.

One day her temper exploded when she learned that patients had been selling gift medicines and food on the black market. She assembled all patients able to walk and lectured them sternly until a self-appointed chief agreed to find and correct the culprits.

But her colleagues knew that underneath the brusqueness was a heart of tender compassion. Once a man came for help from a faraway tribe. Though Dr. Ardel couldn't speak his language, she tried very hard to help him. After he stabbed himself to

---

*A panel of leprosy experts at the Eighth International Congress on Leprology, 1963, in Rio de Janeiro outlined these new directions in leprosy control:

1. Indiscriminate and compulsory isolation for leprosy patients is condemned.

2. There is no need of special institutions for children of leprosy patients, but when placement in an institution is necessary, they should be admitted in institutions for general child care.

3. The separation of a baby from its lepromatous (acutely ill) parent is, therefore, not generally recommended, and leprosy must be taken as a calculated risk and other methods of protection attempted.

4. Children with leprosy should never be denied the right to education. For lepromatous children it may be necessary that special classes be provided. If the number of children is high, special schools may have to be maintained in sanatoria, and the children can be hospitalized during the school year.

The Ban Me Thuot Christian and Missionary Alliance leprosarium in central South Viet Nam where Dr. Ardel Vietti served until her capture by Viet Cong rebels. The leprosarium remains in "unsafe" territory. (Christian and Missionary Alliance photo)

Leprosy victims arriving at the leprosarium—their last hope —before Dr. Vietti's capture. Less than 10 miles from this spot six Alliance missionaries were killed by Communist soldiers in 1968. (Christian and Missionary Alliance photo)

Above: Dr. Vietti examines the disfigured hands of a leprosy sufferer. (Christian and Missionary Alliance photo) **Right:** After the destructive Communist offensive against Saigon in 1968, the 52-member Faith Baptist Church built housing and provided food and medical care for 3,000 refugees. Here a Vietnamese doctor holds clinic among some of the children. (Southern Baptist Foreign Mission Board photo)

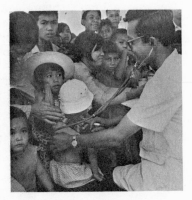

death in a fit of depression, the nurses heard her sobbing in bitter disappointment.

Periodically she went on long survey trips to mount the second line of attack. She traveled by motor bike and sometimes by launch up and down rushing rivers punctuated by dangerous rapids. She brushed off warnings of possible capture by Viet Cong guerillas with a smiling declaration that it was important to find leprosy victims in early stages of infection.

One of the Alliance nurses usually accompanied her on these trips to hold on-the-spot clinics in which everyone in a village was given the "feather treatment."

They carried a bundle of white strips of cloth. When a tribesman stepped forward to be examined, the nurse tied the cloth around his eyes, then Dr. Ardel tickled him with the feather. The nurse stood by with a chart to mark any places where the patient could not feel. When the examination was completed, the nurse dropped the cloth around the person's neck. Not until every villager wore a "necktie" did the feather treatment stop.

Those who tested positive (no feeling on one or more areas of the body) were given blood tests. Patients whose blood smears showed evidence of leprosy bacilli were given sulfones on the spot and instructed to come to one of six outpatient centers for further treatments.

In one village Dr. Ardel and nurse "Dixie" Oliver found 30 percent incidence of leprosy. Though 10 percent was never unusual, when they started back to the leprosy hospital with a group of seriously ill patients, the doctor remarked to Dixie, "This has to be the highest incidence of leprosy anywhere in the world."

Dr. Ardel was both fascinated and horrified by the religious sacrifices of the pagan Radays. One dark night she stayed in a village and watched a ceremony. After a water buffalo was tied by the neck to a stump, a group of drunken tribesmen began dancing to the beat of drums around the frightened beast, hacking at the animal's tendons with machetes. She saw the tortured beast wobble on broken, bleeding stumps of legs, then finally collapse to the ground while the men danced about jabbing spears into it from every angle. The Radays believed that the more a sacrificial animal was tortured, the more the spirits would be pleased. When the crazed animal was writhing in its death throes, the Radays shoved a hollow bamboo tube through a spear hole into the heart. Men caught the spurting blood in bowls, then sprinkled the blood on the sick, whom the spirits were believed to have entered.

The sprinkling completed, the men held their bloody spears and machetes aloft and cried, "Spirits of the North, South, East, and West; spirits of the trees, rivers, rocks, and hills; all spirits big and small—come see the blood of our sacrifice and bring us good crops and health."

It was enough, Dr. Ardel and her colleagues agreed, to make angels weep. "We must help them to know the truth that can set them free," she declared.

Thousands of Radays were coming to know the truth, and many of them were victims of leprosy who had first heard the gospel after receiving loving care at the leprosarium. One patient became a noted evangelist, hunting down outcasts in the forest to tell them where they could find both physical and spiritual hope. More young men came to the Raday Bible school in Ban Me Thuot to prepare for pastoral ministries among their own people.

Dr. Ardel and the other missionaries knew Viet Cong agents were active in the jungles surrounding the hospital. The VCs, in an attempt to exploit long-standing tribal grievances against the central government in Saigon, were anxious to win the Radays and other tribespeople over to their side. But since they knew that the Alliance missionaries were highly admired by the tribal leaders, they hesitated to attack them as they were attacking other Americans.

Among those who came to the leprosarium to help with the growing ministry were the Archie Mitchell family and young Dan Gerber, a Mennonite peace worker. Dan supervised the agricultural program for patients and tribal employees. He also fell in love with one of Dr. Ardel's best nurses, Ruth Wilting. After the couple announced their engagement, Dr. Ardel helped celebrate by cooking some of her renowned "wop" spaghetti and salad.

In April 1962, while Dan and Ruth were planning their wedding, the doctor accompanied an ill missionary home to the United States—her first trip back since going to the field. Dr. John Dick, stationed at Nha Trang, agreed to care for critically ill patients while she was gone.

Dr. Ardel spent most of her two months away at the U.S. Public Health Hospital for leprosy patients in Carville, Louisiana, learning about new drugs and new methods of treating the disease. Shortly before her scheduled return, she visited her family and church friends in Houston. One evening she sat in the back of the Alliance church and whispered to her long-time friend and former Sunday school teacher, Mrs. Billie Pettis, "God's eternal purpose is to conform me to the likeness of Christ. He's going to put me in the place to do that."

Despite pleas to stay on for her upcoming furlough, Dr. Ardel flew back to Viet Nam in May, arriving just in time to help Archie and Betty Mitchell celebrate their fifteenth wedding anniversary.

Eager to share what she had learned at Carville, she scheduled a medical seminar the last week in May for Alliance personnel. Though Dr. John Dick had planned to attend, a last-minute check showed there was no lodging available for his family. He made a business trip to Dalat instead.

Early Wednesday morning, May 30, Archie Mitchell and young Tim Ziemer, son of translator Robert Ziemer, discovered three burned bridges on the road into Ban Me Thuot. At one of them a crudely scrawled sign read: FIX THIS BRIDGE AND OFF WILL GO YOUR HEAD.

Mitchell talked with Dr. Ardel and other missionaries. They decided the Viet Cong meant the warning for someone else. Dan Gerber jumped on his tractor and made a temporary road around two of the bridgeouts.

After finishing work late that afternoon, Dan took his fiancée for a walk. Dr. Ardel was in her room nursing a painful leg ulcer.

Just before twilight she heard a babble of voices outside. Opening the door, she saw two Vietnamese men in black pajamas— Viet Cong! "Come with us, doctor," one ordered.

Dr. Ardel followed the two guerillas to where their companions held other missionaries at gunpoint. The Communists demanded and received keys to the hospital pickup. Then they ordered Dr. Ardel, Archie Mitchell, and Dan Gerber into the truck. "The rest of you do not leave until tomorrow morning," the VC leader said. "And never come back!" Then the attackers drove away with their captives.

The missionaries who were left behind departed in jeeps the next morning and notified authorities in Ban Me Thuot. U.S. military advisors joined South Vietnamese soldiers in a search-and-rescue operation. They found the truck dismantled and buried. But when they got within sight of the abductors and saw they had been heavily reinforced, the U.S. commander reluctantly decided not to attack. Through Saigon, he notified Alliance headquarters in New York that a rescue attempt would only bring heavy loss of life.

The missionaries who had been living on the hospital grounds moved into houses within the Alliance compound at Ban Me Thuot. Raday nurses continued to keep the hospital open, using medicines and supplies obtained from the mission clinic in Ban Me Thuot.

During the years following the abductions, reports filtered in from the jungle telling of tribespeople who had seen the three captives alive in a mobile Viet Cong prison camp. Early in 1967 a Raday tribeswoman said she had seen two white men and a white woman with a group of Viet Cong. The white woman had asked her for a Bible. Later, Allied soldiers overran a Viet Cong jungle hospital and found prescriptions which they said only an American doctor could have written.

Alliance leaders kept up a continual diplomatic offensive. They asked the American, International, Cambodian, and North Viet Nam Red Cross organizations to help. They appealed for intervention by Viet Cong political representatives in Cuba and Algiers. They sent requests to Russia, Switzerland, and the International Control Commission, set up in 1954 to supervise the neutrality between North and South Viet Nam.

Betty Mitchell and her children left Ban Me Thuot in October 1967 for an overdue furlough. She arrived home still confident that her husband, Dr. Ardel, and Dan were going to be released. Back in Ban Me Thuot, Dan's fiancée, nurse Ruth Wilting, resumed work on her wedding dress. "I believe Dan and I will be reunited soon," she said.

January 30, 1968, the Communists launched their now infamous Tet offensive. Scores of missionaries huddled in bunkers and private quarters in major cities while fierce battles raged outside. But only the Ban Me Thuot group suffered fatalities. Caught in a battle zone between defending South Vietnamese and attacking Viet Cong and North Vietnamese, six were killed, two wounded, and two captured. Bob Ziemer, the chief translator of the Raday Bible, was murdered while pleading for mercy. Nurse Ruth Wilting was machine-gunned as she leaped into a bunker fashioned from a garbage pit only a few hours earlier. Newly arrived missionaries Ed and Ruth Thompson died in the pit with her. Carolyn Griswold, who had been a close single girl friend of Dr. Ardel's, and her father died from an explosive charge set in their house.

Wycliffe Bible translator Hank Blood, who lived a few blocks away, was taken captive along with Betty Olsen, a new Alliance nurse.

Only two months before the Tet attack, Betty Olsen had written Medical Assistance Programs in Wheaton, Illinois, asking for a shipment of medicines to treat leprosy patients in the name of Dr. Ardel Vietti. "It is true she is still in Viet Cong hands, going on six years now," the nurse said, "but we would appreciate it if you would honor her name and help us secure these items."

In the 1968 Tet attack on Ban Me Thuot, the Communists took captive along with Hank Blood and Betty Olsen about fifty Raday Christians. Some of these were set free in succeeding weeks and returned with news that Hank and Betty were living but under heavy guard. Later, a Raday pastor who escaped after learning he was going to be executed returned with news that the two missionary captives were alive but that Hank was suffering from a kidney ailment.

There is less evidence that Dr. Ardel, Dan Gerber, and Archie Mitchell are still alive. Alliance missionaries both in the United States and Viet Nam hold divided opinions. One told me, "We believe the 1962 captives are being used to treat wounded and sick Viet Cong." Betty Mitchell, who returned to Ban Me Thuot in 1969, declared, "I feel certain that Ardel, Dan, and Archie are alive and will be released." But another missionary in Viet Nam told me frankly, "We'd like to be as optimistic as Betty Mitchell. But with jungle diseases, shortage of medicines, fighting, and saturation bombing by American planes, I don't see how they can have survived."

Dr. Ardel's medical certificates and licenses have been returned to her mother in Houston. Mrs. Vietti wrote the sender, "I'll keep them, but I know when Ardel comes back she won't be here long."

Alliance churches, of course, still pray for Dr. Ardel Vietti and her colleagues. After a prayer service for the captives at Central Alliance Church in Lincoln, Nebraska, teenager Miss Gale Harris wrote an open letter to the captives:

"Accepting Jesus as my Lord has revolutionized my life. . . . Knowing you also have chosen him as Lord and have been willing to follow where he leads, I can understand why you are mission-

aries. It was but another step as a disciple to follow the Lord
to Viet Nam. You knew that to follow him meant to count all
else loss, and that it might mean death. Still, you were willing.
This is why I can easily understand that when you were taken
captive by some whose lives God wants to capture for his glory
you might have said, even if escape seemed possible, 'We choose
to stay.'

"Has there been a choice flanked by the promise of freedom
only at your denial of the Lord Jesus Christ? Then it makes our
hearts rise in praise that what has happened to you, as to Paul,
has caused rather 'the furtherance of the Gospel.' If there was
no demand for an open denial—just a chance to escape—surely
you considered the plight of your captors. Maybe the love of
God toward them bound you tighter than any ropes of rebels
could.

"Jesus also said, 'Everyone that hath forsaken houses, or brethren, or sisters, or father, or mother, or wife, or children, or lands,
for my name's sake, shall receive an hundredfold, and shall in-
herit everlasting life' (Matt. 19:29). Did you choose to forsake
all for Jesus' sake? Did you choose to remain captive, so that
by giving up your lives others might know the love of God and
his Son, Jesus Christ? Have you had to choose between 'home
and kindred, friends and dear ones' and the service of him who
is altogether worthy?"

Perhaps Dr. Ardel Vietti and her colleagues have already made
these choices in the affirmative. Perhaps they are dead for having
so decided. Perhaps they are still living. But whether she is
dead or alive, Dr. Ardel has more than fulfilled the prediction
of her pastor that "this stubborn girl will stick."

10.

Doctor of New Hope

JEROME FLUTH, M.D.

Dr. Jerry Fluth has two strikes against him.

He is a white medical missionary from the United States serving in Cameroon, Africa, a new country which has few national doctors and a $110 per capita annual income. He is a citizen of a powerful foreign power that has sent thousands of missionaries to Africa while discriminating against black men at home.

He is a foreign missionary, a service vocation once held in highest esteem by Africans, but now subject to criticism and even identification with imperialism. The time of the "white master" has gone and he must be a co-worker with black men who perceive immediately any spirit of condescension.

The lanky young 6'2" doctor is very much aware of the rising currents of nationalism that swirl about him. He recognizes that he is constantly on trial before black staff and patients at the 58-bed New Hope Settlement Hospital in western Cameroon where he is the only doctor. He is quick to admit, "I cannot treat, hire, fire, or discipline an African in the same way I can a colleague or another white. The African would immediately say I was anti-black. I must be very careful about salary demands, even when the budget can't bear them. Blunt refusals will bring charges that I am 'keeping Africans down.' But with Cameroonians, it's different. They can deal with their own people without fear of such criticism."

Easy-going and quiet-spoken, Dr. Fluth talked with a relaxed grin about relationships between missionaries and nationals. "We're sort of victims of our own success. We've been training Africans to take over, and now that they are, it's hard for us to adjust. But," and his eyes hardened, "I take issue with people who blame missionaries for all the problems of Africa.

"The problems of a continent where over twenty new nations have become independent since 1960 are terribly complex. You can't blame missionaries for all of them. It's wrong to judge past missionaries in the light of today's world. What I've read of their writings and journals indicates that they were better men than they are given credit for today. Certainly they were ahead of their time in educating Africans for leadership."

Dr. Fluth's hospital is in West Cameroon, the smaller of two states that make up the 5.6 million population Federal Republic of Cameroon. The California-sized country, named for a shellfish and shaped like a sitting dog, lies in the crotch of Central Africa only three degrees above the equator. Bordering six countries, Cameroon's tail curves along the Atlantic with the top of the body ascending along the border of Nigeria-Biafra. The history of Cameroon parallels the history of many other black African countries.

Between the sixteenth and nineteenth centuries, European slave ships plied their nefarious trade off the coast of present-day Cameroon. British Baptist missionaries moved in during the nineteenth century, followed by German farmers and businessmen. In 1884, German explorer Gustav Nachtigal negotiated a treaty of protectorate with the native chief of "Kamerun." The armistice treaty that closed World War I carved the territory into two parts with the coastal one-fifth going to Great Britain and the larger interior to France. Administration of government in each part was placed under the League of Nations.

Following World War II, French Cameroon was a United Nations trust territory until it opted for full independence in 1960. An election split the old British section in two, the northern half voting to join Nigeria and the south uniting with the new nation to form the Federal Republic of Cameroon.

The little country is Africa in miniature. There are lush forests in the south, an elevated grassy plain in the center, rocky crags in the mountainous north and northwest. Volcanic 13,000-foot Mount Cameroon, West Africa's highest peak, is not far from Dr. Fluth's hospital.

Populated by nearly two hundred different tribes, Cameroon

is properly called "the Racial Crossroads of Africa." English is the most commonly spoken language in the west where Dr. Fluth serves; French, in the east.

Over half the people are animists, 10 percent Muslim, 20 percent Catholic, and 15 percent Protestant. Baptists and Presbyterians are especially strong. About seventy missionaries from Dr. Fluth's small North American Baptist General Conference (55,000 U.S. members) work within two Cameroon Baptist conventions that together total 41,000 members.

Baptist work dates from 1848 when British Baptists came as pioneer missionary evangelists. The British remained until the territory became a German colony. However, the first German Baptist missionaries were new United States immigrants sponsored by the North American Baptist General Conference. Baptist missionaries from Germany soon joined them, and they worked together until World War II when the German citizens were interned. A double load was thus placed upon the U.S.-supported missionaries, and in 1943 the Mission sent nurse Laura Reddig home to recruit new workers.

Jerry Fluth, then only nine, lived in Emery, South Dakota, where his father was a safety engineer. The nurse's pictures and pleas for missionaries to come to Cameroon tugged at his heart. He heard Miss Reddig again when she was back on furlough calling for "our first missionary doctor in the Cameroon." One Sunday after a church play in which Jerry played the role of a missionary doctor, one of the deacons patted him on the head and said, "You'll be out there one day."

The first Baptist missionary doctor to Cameroon was Dr. Leslie M. Chaffee, appointed when Jerry Fluth was fourteen. Although he could not be the first, he continued to pursue the goal inspired by Laura Reddig. "I had," he recalled, "no sudden experience or dramatic revelation of God's will, but rather a growing feeling and awareness that this was God's plan for my life. I wanted not just to be a doctor with a practice in Africa, but a missionary doctor."

So that it would be convenient for Jerry to attend the University of Minnesota, his family moved to Minneapolis. There he taught Sunday school, held leadership posts in youth groups, and served as a counselor at youth camps. While at camp one summer he struck up an acquaintance with a tall blonde girl counselor. Friendship ripened into love, and Jerry and farm girl Ramona Adam had a June wedding in 1955, one year before he

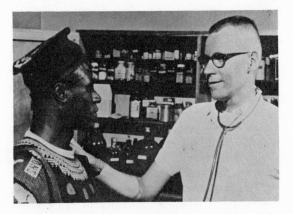

Dr. Jerome Fluth, representative of the North American Baptist General Conference in the Cameroons, confers with a national hospital colleague. "We're victims of our own success," Dr. Fluth says. "We've been training Africans to take over, and now that they are, it's hard for us to adjust." (North American Baptist photo)

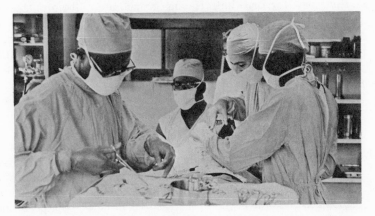

Lutheran missionary and national doctors work together at the Lutheran Hospital in Phebe, Liberia. The "great white father" role of the missionary doctor in Africa is over. (MAP photo)

graduated from the university. She taught school and earned her Ph.T. degree, working to "push hubby through" the University of Minnesota Medical School.

A year's internship at St. Luke's Hospital in Duluth, Minnesota, followed, then a few months of general practice before they departed for Cameroon via Liverpool, England, and a three months course in tropical medicine.

The Fluths and their two small children were welcomed to the Bamenda New Hope Settlement Hospital in the spring of 1961. The hospital, which served both leprosy and general patients, was on a grassy, rolling, two thousand acre "settlement" farm. Leprosy patients needing extended treatment lived about the farm in small houses and tended the herd of four hundred cattle and a coffee plantation which provided desperately needed money for the colony.

There was no point in trying to learn one of the twenty or more tribal languages in the area. Fortunately, most patients spoke a crude form of pidgin English. The culture, however, was something else. Observance of tribal customs required great care. For example, one tribe considered it a gross insult for a man to cross his legs while sitting in the presence of their chief.

The constant association with sensitive blacks was also something new for Dr. Fluth. Having grown up in all-white churches and having had only casual relations with blacks in college and medical school, it was difficult for him to anticipate how black staff members and patients might react in different situations.

Gradually he worked into the routine. He saw leprosy patients on rounds two days a week and general patients three days a week. He made periodic week-long trips along the network of outlying bush clinics. And he kept up a steady schedule of operations, both planned and emergencies.

Hardest was the pressure of being the only doctor at the hospital. Barely twenty-eight, he had to make life and death decisions and, with limited equipment, perform operations for which he had received little training. Once he had to amputate a shoulder at the joint, an operation he had never seen performed.

Even after surgery, hospital rounds, and staff meetings, there were more chores to do. He served as hospital business manager, treasurer, and sometimes as maintenance man. The year after his arrival, he was pouring gasoline into a generator tank when a spark ignited an explosion. Horribly burned over face, arms, and legs, he had to be flown home for emergency treatment and skin grafting.

An emergency call went out asking churches to pray while Dr. Fluth lay in the hospital, his future hanging in the balance. Fortunately the skin grafts took and other burned areas began healing. He applied for a year's surgical training but was turned down because of the fear that unhealed areas on his face and hands might be a hazard to patients. However, he was permitted to take a year's residency in physical medicine and patient rehabilitation.

In 1963 the Fluths returned to Cameroon. "I am seeing patients with different eyes," he told his wife after a few days' work. "I understand now what it means to suffer."

He adjusted quickly to the demanding routine. He felt deep satisfaction in seeing patients profess faith in Christ and return home to evangelize their relatives. Ramona Fluth was happy in her women's work and the care of their three small children.

Dr. Fluth's load became easier when a missionary businessman arrived to relieve him of much of the administrative responsibility. A credit union was formed among staff and patients. Dr. Fluth, the new manager, and the three missionary nurses met regularly with the African staff to discuss mutual problems.

The fever of nationalism continued to rise. Missionaries agreed with the goal of national control of institutions, yet feared the result of sudden change. Direction of Baptist mission schools in the Cameroon was yielded to an educational authority composed jointly of selected missionaries and national church leaders. The government took over operation of rural leprosy clinics which had been related to the New Hope Hospital. New labor laws compelled the New Hope Hospital to raise African staff salaries 30 to 40 percent, forcing cutbacks in buying desperately needed equipment. Repeatedly, Dr. Fluth was asked, "When are you going to train a Cameroonian doctor to take charge?"

While home recently for his first regular furlough and for surgical training at the Mayo Clinic, he frankly admitted the "growing pains" caused by surging nationalism. "We're enlarging our Cameroonian staff to meet both needs and the demands of nationalism. We're getting a physical therapist and a shoemaker, both Africans, who will help tremendously in rehabilitating our leprosy patients. But we don't have a Cameroonian doctor in sight yet. There isn't even a degree granting institution in the country."

Where does he find strength to continue serving in the face of pressing needs and demanding change? "Faith," he declared. "We don't find God in our wisdom, but in our faith. Once we have the faith, we use our minds under the direction of His Spirit. Then we praise Him for what is accomplished."

11.

The Missionary Dentist Who Multiplied Himself

AUSTIN ROBBINS, D.D.S.

Lieutenant Austin Robbins, D.D.S., should have been happy. He was married to his high school sweetheart, and they had three delightful children. He had finished his training at the University of Pennsylvania Dental School less than three years before, and he was to muster out of the Navy in just a few weeks. He looked forward to beginning dental practice with his soon-to-retire father in New Jersey.

But the ambitious young dentist was disturbed. Finally he asked the pastor of the First Brethren Church in Long Beach, California, for an appointment.

"I've got this feeling that I ought to do something," he told the pastor. "But I don't know what. Shirley and I are more active in the church than ever. The future never looked so bright."

"Austin," the pastor said kindly, "you think you want the Lord to show you what to do, and then let you decide whether you'll do it or not. You should say, 'Lord, whatever you want me to do, I'll do it.' Then it's up to Him to show you."

"I think you're right," the dentist said with a wry grin. "I'll pray that way."

A few Sundays later a Brethren medical missionary addressed the Long Beach congregation. Dr. Harold Mason spoke compellingly about church growth in then French Equatorial Africa, their denomination's biggest overseas field. Afterwards, Dr. Robbins walked up to greet the visiting speaker.

Before his turn came, he overheard a woman speaking to the

doctor about her cousin, a dentist missionary in South
America. "For forty years we've been praying that the Lord
would send a dentist to us in Africa," the missionary com-
mented.

Without thinking, Dr. Robbins blurted, "I'm a dentist."

The missionary doctor looked at him as if he had just discovered a diamond. "I'd like to talk to you about our work. Can
you imagine a million people without a dentist? Oh, sure there
are a few French dentists there. But they treat only Europeans
and a handful of well-to-do Africans. There's not one African
dentist in our area—not one."

Only a month remained until Dr. Robbins was scheduled to
leave the Navy. During these days he and his wife prayed and
talked about Dr. Mason's challenge. Every time he thought
about joining his father in practice in New Jersey, an inner
voice seemed to whisper, "I need a dentist in Africa."

Three months later the Robbinses were in Winona Lake, In-
diana, where the dentist enrolled in Grace Theological Seminary
for the three-year course. Two years later, in 1959, the missionary board of the National Fellowship of Brethren Churches suggested they go to Africa "while the door was still open." The
year before, the Central African Republic had become an
autonomous state within the French community of nations. It
was to become fully independent the next year and might place
restrictions on the entry of new missionaries.

The Robbinses arrived there in October 1959, just as the
steamy rainy season was ending. They moved into a mission
house at Yaloke and began language study. A glance at a map
showed that they were indeed deep in the heart of Africa. Lying
about one thousand miles equidistant from the Atlantic and
Indian Ocean, the C.A.R. bordered five countries, all throbbing
with the spirit of nationalism. Hilly savanna stretched north to
Chad and east to Sudan. Tropical rain forest spread southwest
to the Cameroons and south to the two Congos. The landlocked
country, slightly smaller than Texas, had no railroads.

At that time the poverty-stricken C.A.R. had less than $100
per capita income and over 90 percent illiteracy. The French
colonial government had regularly spent only 1 percent of its
budget for education. Largely agricultural, with poor soil and
without a port, the country could hardly compete with its
neighbors. It seemed ironic to the Robbinses that diamonds, the

Dr. Austin Robbins,
representative of the
Foreign Missionary Society
of The Brethren Church,
broke new ground in
training African
dentists.

Missionary dentistry
has become a new
frontier of service
for many missions.
Here Southern Baptist
Dr. Howard D. McCamey
explores the mouth
of a Nigerian.
(Southern Baptist
Foreign Mission Board
photo)

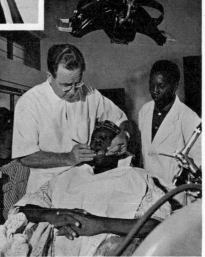

main export, were going from one of the poorest countries in the world to the wealthiest people in other countries.

The founders of the Brethren Mission had entered the country in 1919. While moving up a treacherous river, pioneer James Gribble had written, "Our going forth is for the purpose of putting the gospel to a test among the pagan people . . . It is not we who are on trial, it is the gospel which we preach." Introduced through evangelistic, educational, and medical ministries, the gospel passed the test. Over two hundred and fifty congregations sprang up, led by graduates of the Mission's Bible school.

The Robbinses studied French and the Sango trade language for the first year. Then they moved to the crossroads town of Boguila where Dr. Robbins set up his clinic in the Brethren hospital. He quickly recognized that the needs were overwhelming. The bush people ate unrefined foods and had few cavities, but they suffered from teeth mutilated and filed to meet tribal customs. Most had terrible gum infections, the worst he had ever seen. Africans who had moved into the larger cities had even more severe problems because their teeth presented little resistance to the decay caused by a civilized diet.

Effective dental hygiene was practiced only by the missionaries. The Africans used a crude toothbrush, made of wood and slivered on the end to make it bristly. Toothpaste was as rare as moon rocks; the use of fluoride and other preventive measures were unknown.

Dr. Robbins prayed and pondered what to do. Should he continue work at the hospital, treating patients as they came to him? Or become a circuit rider and take dentistry and Bible teaching to people in the bush? Or train Christian Africans to take care of the dental needs of their own people? The history of the Brethren churches in the C.A.R. showed that their greatest growth had come under the leadership of trained Africans. The membership of the churches had doubled during a ten-year period after the Bible school opened. Mission-trained medics in outlying bush dispensaries had stretched the arm of Christian healing to thousands whom the two mission doctors could not possibly reach. Could African dentists also be trained to do the same?

When he asked where could he find a model, other missionaries directed him to Dr. Ted Shanks, a Presbyterian dentist who had started a school in neighboring Cameroon. Dr. Shanks's setup was impressive. He had good equipment and eager students. "I'm training them to be auxiliary personnel," Dr. Shanks explained. "They will work under the supervision of qualified dentists."

Dr. Robbins was not so impressed that this was the way. He felt that the sooner Africans could take charge, the better it would be for the growth of the churches and their healing ministries.

While the Robbinses were home on their first furlough, Dr. Robbins firmed up plans for his dental school. He made arrangements with Medical Assistance Programs (MAP) for donation of medicines and equipment. He spoke in Brethren churches and received money pledges for a building.

Back in Africa for a second term, Dr. Robbins worked through an African board of pastors and laymen to secure permission from the government to begin the school. While a small cement block building was under construction, new graduates from the Brethren high school vied for admittance. On the basis of qualifying examinations which covered math, reading comprehension in French and Sango, writing ability, and manual dexterity, four young men were selected for the three-year course.

The first year they studied basic science courses and an introduction to dentistry. The second year they tackled pathology, anesthesia, extractions, fillings, and began work on patients under the close supervision of Dr. Robbins. The third year they did more patient work and were introduced to oral surgery and preparation of dentures.

One day the district governor stopped by to check on the work of the American missionaries. Pressure had been mounting to cancel the residence permits of foreigners who were of "no social benefit" to the country. The governor agreed that the nurses and doctors were certainly wanted. "But what use are you to us?" he asked Dr. Robbins.

The missionary dentist took the African administrator through the clinic-school and showed him the mouths of several patients who were waiting to see the student dentists. Then he introduced him to the students and explained that they would become the country's first native dentists.

A smile wreathed the official's face. "Good," he declared. "You are just the kind of foreigner we need. One who will show Africans how to do things for themselves."

The patient load greatly increased during the third year as news spread of the enlarged services. Adult Africans with teeth mutilated since childhood came in for extractions and subsequently left with dentures to show off in their villages. The professor's services continued to be in demand, particularly by Europeans living in the area. Because his time was limited, he gave non-emergency cases the choice of waiting six to eight months or sitting in a student's chair. Many chose the students.

One was a young French woman who was emotionally distraught and apprehensive about dental work. Dr. Robbins happened to pass by the chair and overheard the African student telling her that Christ could calm her fears.

"What a switch," he exclaimed to his wife afterwards. "An African professional witnessing to a European patient! What a reversal of past tradition!"

The four students graduated in May 1968. Dr. Robbins proudly introduced them as the "first African dentists in the Central African Republic." The new dentists were required to work at the Brethren hospital for a few months; then two moved out to work at the hospital dispensaries in the C.A.R., and two went to neighboring Chad where the need was just as great. In October 1969 the Voice of America carried a broadcast telling of the work of the Chad dentists.

As his family packed for their second furlough in 1968, Dr. Robbins said, "I don't feel badly about being away this time. I'm leaving four dentists behind."

The two oldest Robbins children, Bruce and Susan, entered high school. Patrice, the youngest, was ready for seventh grade. Dr. Robbins joined the faculty of the University of Pennsylvania School of Dental Medicine where he anticipates getting "more experience in dental education" and "recruiting some missionary dentists."

"Missionary dentistry is fifty years behind missionary medicine," he told me in an interview. "But I don't see going to another country just to practice. We should go to train nationals.

"Dentistry is ready-made for Christian witnessing. The Christian dentist has person-to-person contact with his patients at regular intervals for weeks at a time. The Africans take more time with patients than we do. Two hours is the usual length of an appointment. They do not have the time-saving equipment and personal assistance the American dentist has in his office. But this added time allows them more opportunity to share the gospel. And isn't that the main purpose of a Christian's life—to share the gospel?"

12.

Fence Builders on the Cliff

WARREN AND GRETCHEN
BERGGREN, M.D.s

Pledging continued prayers, the Congolese pastors had anointed their "Dr. Warren" with oil and left. The kerosene lamp splashed dark shadows on the mud ceiling of the mission bedroom. Beside her husband's bed Dr. Gretchen Berggren sat praying for wisdom and that their close friend, Dr. Paul Carlson, would arrive soon. She had done all she could to arrest the malaria and pneumonia that had pushed her husband to the brink of death. Dr. Helen Berquist had arrived to take over responsibilities at their mission hospital in the Ubangi.

As the long hours dragged by, she recalled happier times when she and Warren were students together at the University of Nebraska Medical School. They had met at a Christian Medical Society meeting and discovered that they both came from rural Nebraska communities, were of similar church background, and were interested in medical missions. After that, Warren—three years ahead in school—managed to find ample time to "help" the vivacious Gretchen with her studies. Following graduation and internship, Warren had gone to the Congo for a year before joining her in Brussels for further tropical medicine study and marriage.

Now it looked as if their second term might be cut short. "He's made so many plans," she thought as she remembered the plans for a pilot program in community health. "Dear Lord, please help him."

A few minutes later she heard a truck bouncing down the

muddy road. She ran to the door to greet the missionary doctor who had driven all night over muddy rain-forest roads to be at his friend's side.

Dr. Paul Carlson, a first-term missionary for the Evangelical Covenant Church of America, checked the sick doctor's thready pulse, raspy breathing, and heart sounds. Drawing back, he put a strong arm around Gretchen Berggren's tired shoulders. "Let's pray, before we make any decisions," he requested. Then, "Get some rest and let me take over. God will help us pull him through."

Under the care of his doctor wife and Dr. Carlson, Dr. Warren Berggren rallied. They knew what their patient should do next. "Go home and recuperate," Dr. Carlson said. "But how I wish you could stay."

Warren Berggren nodded weakly. The two doctors had hoped to establish a medical center in the needy Ubangi region with modern equipment for use by a team of doctors making round-robin visits to satellite "bush" stations. Congolese nurses, midwives, and lab technicians could come to the center for medical and spiritual training. And it would be a base for launching pilot programs in public health, desperately needed since the departure of five hundred Belgian doctors with the advent of independence.

The Berggrens returned home in April 1964, before the infamous atrocities against missionaries began in the Congo. Shortly after both enrolled in Harvard University's School of Public Health for graduate study, they received news that Dr. Carlson had been condemned to be executed as a "spy" in Stanleyville. In a desperate attempt to save Dr. Carlson, three of their friends at Harvard—a Protestant, a Catholic, and a Buddhist—voluntarily called United Nations Secretary-General U Thant and were assured that he would try to intervene.

But hours before Thanksgiving, they heard the report that shocked the world: Dr. Carlson had been shot to death as a rescue force of paratroopers were dropping into the city. Along with hundreds of other medical missionaries, the Berggrens dedicated themselves to renewed service for God and suffering humanity.

Believing that they could be of greatest benefit in preventing disease, the Berggrens completed their studies at Harvard. Dr. Warren Berggren added a doctorate in public health to the master's degree he had previously acquired. His wife also earned her master's at Harvard. During this three-year period, their second daughter was born.

Because of Warren's delicate health, return to the Congo did not seem advisable. Then a new door opened. Dr. Larry Mellon, founder and director of the Albert Schweitzer Hospital in Haiti, asked Warren to direct his hospital's advance into community health and preventive medicine. The Harvard School of Public Health appointed Warren as assistant professor of public health and planned to send students to Haiti to train under his tutelage.

Albert Schweitzer Hospital was well known to the Berggrens. It had been built in tribute to the famous doctor-scholar by Dr. and Mrs. Mellon after they had read several of his books. At thirty-eight, Larry Mellon had reentered college to become a doctor; while still in medical school, he and his wife, by establishing and placing their fortune in the Grant Foundation, initiated steps to assure the hospital's construction. Situated in the picturesque Artibonite Valley of Haiti, the 133-bed hospital serves an area where there formerly were only two dispensaries for the some eighty thousand peasants plagued by poverty-related diseases.

The Berggrens hoped to stay for a three-year term, retaining a leave-of-absence relationship with their Evangelical Free Church mission board. The nonsectarian hospital did not include the same kind of evangelistic outreach as a traditional missionary hospital. But they could still witness in private conversation and by the example of their concern.

In late 1967 they arrived in Port-au-Prince, the capital of Haiti. The Vermont-sized Caribbean country occupies the western third of the island of Hispaniola, and at that time it had a population of 4.7 million people. With a per capita annual income of $80 per year and illiteracy standing at 90 percent, the small nation was considered by some to be the poorest in the Western hemisphere. A Land Rover carried the Berggrens along a dusty road to the hospital 90 miles inland.

Three months of intensive study showed them the major medical problems were tetanus of the newborn, malnutrition, tuberculosis, and gastroenteritis. The hospital was always full to overflowing, and people were being turned away every day.

The Berggrens decided to tackle tetanus of the newborn first.

The infectious disease, known also as lockjaw and often fatal, is caused by the tetanus germ entering the body through a cut or injury. The resulting convulsions and severe muscle spasms were heartbreaking to observe in an infant. Many of 455 such cases admitted to the hospital during 1967 had died.

The Berggrens directed a house-to-house census of nine thousand people in the twenty-three villages nearest the hospital. Census takers asked mothers how many children had died, at what time, and from what. The check showed that twenty years before over one-fourth of the babies born alive had died from newborn tetanus. The hospital's prenatal services and instruction of "granny" midwives not to put charcoal or other contaminated materials on the umbilical cord had lowered the death rate, but the disease was still widespread.

Results from health programs in Colombia indicated that the best control was to vaccinate potential mothers. A series of three immunizations would protect both the mother and all newborns. After five years, the mother would need only a booster injection.

Clinic tables were set up outside the hospital and in marketplaces on market days. When a woman was vaccinated, she received a vaccination card, and her record was entered in a register for future reference.

Next, volunteer workers were handed census lists of women who had not been vaccinated during the first census in their villages. Each worker bringing in all on his list received a transistor radio as a special award.

Enthusiasm mounted among the peasant women as the program progressed. On mornings when a second shot was due for many of the women, the Berggrens would arrive at a marketplace at 5:30 to find as many as four thousand people pushing and shoving to reach the tables. Using a jet-injector, the team Dr. Warren had trained could handle this huge crowd.

By the end of 1968, records showed sixty-five thousand people had received twice that number of tetanus vaccinations. Cases of newborn tetanus admitted to the hospital had fallen by one-third. Dr. Warren Berggren calculated that by staying at that level, twenty-one thousand bed days could be saved during the next five years for hospital care for other diseases.

Malnutrition was the next target for attack by the Berggrens. Three hundred severely malnourished children were being brought to the hospital's pediatric clinic each week, many of whom bore the sad symptoms of kwashiorkor, a disease caused by protein deficiency: low weight (an eighteen-month-old child might weigh ten pounds or less), swelling of the feet and

Dr. Warren Berggren,
member of the Evangelical
Free Church, has pioneered
new programs in infant nutrition
and preventive medicine
in Haiti.
(MAP photo)

Above: Life-saving inoculations
against neonatal tetanus are
part of the community health program
for Albert Schweitzer Hospital in Haiti
where Drs. Warren and Gretchen Berggren
serve. Dr. Berggren (r) is shown
receiving a shipment from a member
of MAP's board, Dr. G. A. Hemwall
of Chicago. **Right:** Mothers register
for Dr. Warren Berggren's
nutrition clinic in Haiti.
(MAP photos)

ankles, poor appetite, and weak, wasted muscles (some were unable to walk). A typical kwashiorkor child had been taken from its mother's breast too soon and given little or no milk or protein afterwards. Children blind from vitamin A deficiency were seen as well.

The mothers who had brought children to the clinic had been told to "give your child plenty of milk, eggs, and meat" and sent home with a package of powdered milk. But most of them could not follow these instructions even if they had remembered them. Such foods were either not available or were not included in family meal planning. The average Haitian family has meat once a week and depends on vegetable protein sources.

Clearly, something more had to be done.

News came that the Haitian Bureau of Nutrition had a unique program inspired by nutrition experts in another part of the country. Dr. Warren Berggren visited a "nutrition recuperation center" and saw how the problem might be solved. A trained woman was spending three months with mothers of thirty children, teaching them how to prepare balanced meals in cooking pots over open fires. The ingredients were locally available and within the budget of the average family.

Albert Schweitzer Hospital had already decided to train a cadre of Haitian lady monitors to teach mothers to cook under typical home conditions at a cost of nine cents per person per day. Readily available protein-rich red beans and yellow sweet potatoes, rich in needed vitamin A and better than the more regularly eaten white sweet potatoes, were utilized in ample quantities.

The "nutrition teachers" were then sent to villages to work with selected mothers for a three-month period in an established "center." At the end of the time, they asked the mothers, "Do your children look better now? Have we done anything here that you can't do in your home?"

A "mothers' retreat" was opened near the hospital where small groups of women helped prepare balanced meals for their children at the same time that they were receiving nutrition education. These mothers went home after three days, with instructions to return at regularly scheduled times for evaluation of their children.

A trained staff member reached more mothers in the hospital by holding fifteen-minute nutrition interviews with two or three women at a time. Here, as elsewhere, the emphasis was upon balanced meals which the mothers could prepare in their humble homes.

Comparing his work in the Congo to the community health efforts in Haiti, Dr. Warren Berggren says, "There we had a crisis every day. We felt a sense of accomplishment with every dramatic success. Here the work is much less dramatic. But we're reaping some exciting rewards. One village center," he notes, "can train twelve mothers for three months for what it costs the hospital to treat one severely malnourished child. Our brief 'mothers' retreat' can teach five hundred mothers for what it costs to treat ten children for malnutrition in the hospital.

"In the past, medical missionaries have spent more time curing than preventing disease. Most will probably continue working this way because it gives a better chance to build a personal relationship with each patient. But I do think we can show just as much—if not more—Christian concern by becoming concerned with the health of large numbers of people.

"It's like the fable Dr. Paul Russell, a great pioneer in malaria control, tells," he says. "After several cars missed a dangerous turn on a road and went over a cliff, an ambulance was stationed at the bottom of the cliff. Why didn't they start by building a fence atop the cliff?"

Drs. Warren and Gretchen Berggren have already started building a new fence atop another cliff. The Schweitzer Hospital in Haiti has been discovering twelve hundred new cases of tuberculosis each year. "What an unnecessary waste of health and life!" he exclaims.

They intend to link this "fence" and others together by building a file of personal health cards for each community. "We will have a record of each person's immunizations, clinic visits and hospitalizations, chart weight, and any other pertinent information available for quick reference," he says. "Why shouldn't we go to this trouble if we really believe God cares for all people?"

13.

Healer of the Oppressed

PAUL BRAND, M.D.

Rain had turned to snow and a bleak wind swept across the nearly deserted Wheaton College campus. Most of its students had gone home for the winter holidays, but in front of the chapel the solitude was broken by a heavy-coated line of doctors, nurses, mission executives, and students interested in missionary medicine who were filing into the empty building. They had given up vacations to attend the Fifth International Conference on Missionary Medicine.

The man they were intent on hearing at this session was Dr. Paul Brand, probably the most honored medical missionary of modern times. The English doctor, who has brought hope to thousands of crippled leprosy victims, is to the fraternity that follows Dr. Luke what Billy Graham is to evangelical ministers. "Paul Brand," chuckled J. Raymond Knighton, the organizer of the convention, "is the only evangelical medical missionary I know ever written up in *Saturday Review* by Norman Cousins."

A quiet, mild-mannered man with thinning hair slipped almost unnoticed to the platform. To the surprise of many, he was introduced as Dr. Brand. "Why, he was with a group of us this morning and we never asked his name," one doctor gasped.

Now the speaker was praying, *Show us ourselves, show us our God, show us how we may serve Him.* The humility of the veteran missionary was obvious as he spoke.

We ordinary human beings with all our frailties are carrying a precious message. . . . We must be concerned with what we

Dr. Paul W. Brand,
probably the most honored
medical missionary of modern times,
is internationally known
for his surgical techniques
in restorative and
rehabilitative surgery
for leprosy victims.

*say, do, and are. . . . The reason for Christ's coming is also the
reason for our being sent. Jesus said, "As my Father hath sent
me, so send I you."*

Many in the audience had read the speaker's life story in the
book *Ten Fingers for God* or as it was condensed in the *Reader's
Digest*. They followed along with him in a deeper dimension
as he spoke.

Paul had been born to Baptist missionaries in a mission out-
post on the rugged Mountains of Death, a malaria-plagued area
of India. When he was nine, he and his sister Connie went to
England to live with relatives while completing their education.
The sad news of their father's death from the dread "black-
water fever" came when Paul was fifteen. Their grieving mother
wrote that she was staying on to carry on the work.

Paul remained in London. He entered medical school and fell
in love with a dark-haired girl student, the daughter of an
English health officer in South Africa. The year Paul was second
in his class, first was Margaret. They were married before he
received his surgical diplomas.

Paul was just beginning practice when an old friend of his
parents arrived. Dr. Robert Cochrane was head of the Christian
Medical College and Hospital in Vellore, India. "We have a
problem, Paul," Dr. Cochrane bluntly declared. "The Indian government has raised medical standards. We must have at least
twelve new teaching doctors."

Paul Brand protested that he didn't have enough experience
to teach. Besides that, his wife was expecting their second
child.

But Dr. Cochrane was not to be deterred. At the age of

thirty-four, Brand left for India, with Margaret following after the birth of their new baby.

Though they planned to stay only a year and then return home, the exhausting but rewarding months filled with twelve-hour teaching and operating days dimmed the desire for professional success in England.

One day Dr. Cochrane invited Paul to "have a look around" the leprosy sanitorium, which by law had to be separate from other facilities. Having been occupied with teaching and surgery, Dr. Brand was happily surprised at what he saw.

He noted most of the patients were not bedfast. They kept the building and grounds immaculate, grew their food, wove cloth for bandages, operated their own shops, even bound their own textbooks. Most were given injections of chaulmoogra oil, since the new sulfone drugs were still in the experimental stage and available only in small amounts. Assured by Dr. Cochrane that he would not "catch" leprosy, Dr. Brand examined a few patients closely. He saw that the disease on some was marked only by a patch of whitish skin or a bald spot. But others stumped around on bandaged, misshapen feet, groped with claw-like hands, lifted deformed faces with ravaged eyes.

Dr. Brand pointed to a twisted hand of one patient. "How did he get that way?"

The older doctor sadly shook his head. "We don't know, Paul. Maybe because no orthopedic surgeon has really studied the deformities that follow leprosy."

Suddenly the younger doctor saw a young man laboring to remove his sandals. Closer inspection revealed that the patient could not open the buckle. "The disease has paralyzed his muscles and damaged his nerves," the older doctor explained. "He has no feeling in his hands or feet."

Curiosity moved Brand to ask the youth, "May I see your hands?"

He pried back the stiff fingers of one hand and put his own hand on the open palm, "Now squeeze and press as hard as you can," he told the patient.

Dr. Brand made a wry face and pulled his hand back. "His hand isn't paralyzed," he told Dr. Cochrane. "He has some good muscles left."

Dr. Brand was all questions as they walked toward Dr. Cochrane's home. Did the paralysis follow a pattern? Why did the fingers and toes of leprosy patients wear away? Might not surgery make a claw-hand usable? Dr. Cochrane's response, "You tell me," and what Dr. Brand saw spurred a new commitment in the younger doctor's mind.

Brand prowled through the medical library but could find nothing about orthopedic surgery on leprosy patients, how the disease might be related to physical deformities, or whether the paralysis followed a certain course.

The next step loomed crystal clear: He must look for answers himself.

"No, the teaching hospital cannot admit leprosy patients," he was told. "The other patients will run away."

Refusing to admit defeat, Dr. Brand recruited a few concerned assistants and began studying patients at the dispensaries where the disease was treated. He identified muscles which were paralyzed and nerves which had thickened and died. While examining two thousand cases, a dramatic truth grew clear: The paralysis did follow an exact pattern. The order in which certain muscles deteriorated was always the same, and certain muscles always remained healthy. Dr. Brand saw hope in surgical treatment.

"Send me a patient whose hands cannot possibly be worse," he asked Dr. Cochrane.

Dr. Cochrane sent a pitifully deformed young Hindu whose hands were unsightly claws and whose feet were so deeply infected with foul-smelling ulcers that the bones could be seen. Worse, he seemed gripped by hopeless despair. Though he came from a good family and was well educated, his family and friends had for all practical purposes cast him on the scrap heap.

The man, named Krishnamurthy, put up no argument against Dr. Brand's proposal to "do some operations" on his hands. "Do as you wish," he said. "They are worth nothing to me."

So, the hospital having finally allowed him two beds for leprosy patients, Dr. Brand and his assistants began their history-making surgery.

He first found a good unparalyzed muscle with a tendon that could be moved. Splitting it into two lengths, he retunneled it to the fingers to take the place of worthless, paralyzed muscles. Then he closed the wounds, applied dressings and a small plaster splint, and waited for the fingers to heal.

Expectations rose when those two fingers healed. Dr. Brand did the same operation on the other two fingers and the thumb, then began physiotherapy. The long-unused joints had to be reconditioned and brain impulses re-educated.

After weeks of waiting—success! Krishnamurthy opened and closed his hand. He grasped objects of varying sizes and shapes —rubber balls, wood blocks, pencils. "Look!" he cried over and over again to Brand.

About a year after the first operation, Krishnamurthy left the hospital with useful hands, healed feet, and a restored outlook on life.

But two months later the Hindu was back, his thin face reflecting bleak despair. "Sahib, Doctor," he told the surgeon, "you gave me bad begging hands."

Dr. Brand listened to his tale of woe. When his hands were claws, people had taken pity and thrown him coins. Now they showed no pity. And because he still bore the marks of leprosy, nobody would give him employment or even shelter.

The man could type, so Dr. Brand put him to work doing small jobs for patients who could afford his services.

Soon another leprosy victim whom Dr. Brand had helped returned for the same reason. "What can I do?" he asked in despondency.

Dr. Brand looked at this second patient who could not type. He would have to be taught a useful trade.

Dr. Brand pictured hundreds of others like this man whose hands, feet, and eyes could be made useful—but who must learn a trade they could pursue without depending on others for employment. Where could he get the money for a place for rehabilitation and training and skilled teachers?

He mentioned the problem to a sympathetic missionary patient who had spent most of her eighty-four years in India. "Mother" Eaton suffered from a painful and incurable rheumatoid arthritis.

"I have about 500 pounds in the bank," she said. "I haven't long to live, so take it and use it."

That conversation marked the beginning of Nava Jeeva Nilayam, the "New Life Center" for rehabilitation of leprosy patients. Dr. Brand won over opposition of fellow doctors to his building the new settlement close to the medical college campus, separated only by a barbed-wire fence. He drew plans and supervised construction of a cluster of mud-walled, grass-roofed buildings and the training shop himself. Back in England he had once worked as a builder.

The surgeon chose the first "citizens" himself: six young boys. Their number quickly doubled to a dozen. The doctor taught them to use carpenter's tools, then showed them how to build toys and jigsaw puzzles that could be marketed. The boys also learned to grow crops and luscious fruit for the colony.

Meanwhile, Dr. Margaret Brand found a meaningful ministry in helping perform eye operations, although she had once said she would work in any department *except* opthalmology. She helped hundreds to see in a day when cataracts alone accounted for more than half a million blind people in India. Dr. Brand's aging mother stayed busy in the foreboding mountains, carrying on the work started by her husband.

Back at the New Life Center, one demanding mystery clamored for an answer: Why did the fingers and toes of leprosy patients waste away? Dr. Brand was inclined not to believe the theory that the process of shortening was directly caused by the disease.

Dr. Brand had already been the first to observe that when patients lost the feeling of pain, they often injured themselves. One day he watched a small boy try to turn the key in a rusty padlock and saw a drop of blood fall to the floor. Grasping the boy's fingers, he saw that the key had torn the skin to the bone. The thought grabbed Brand that the cumulative effect of painless injuries might literally wear away fingers and toes!

He began watching patients more closely and keeping careful records of the condition of their extremities. As his theory advanced in credibility, he educated patients to avoiding injury to insensitive members.

He got them to hold nails with pliers since they could not tell without looking whether a nail was facing the right way. He had tools fitted with round smooth handles and other instruments and objects fitted with safety devices. He sought to account for every blister, callus, scratch, and burn, and then to eliminate the causes. One mysterious injury he traced to a rat that was chewing at night on unfeeling fingers. Cats solved that problem.

In 1952 a representative of the Rockefeller Foundation arrived upon the scene. Dr. Richmond K. Anderson was fascinated by Dr. Brand's work. When Dr. Brand explained that he needed to learn more about fighting the ravages of the disease—plastic surgery, skin grafts, and counteracting nerve paralysis

—Dr. Anderson said, "Go anywhere in the world at our expense where you think you can find help."

Dr. Brand gratefully accepted the offer. After many months of travel, he returned with a fine knowledge of new techniques in surgery. Yet he realized that applying these techniques to leprosy patients would in the main require more research by himself and his own team.

He plodded ahead and shifted major attention to the feet. After a year of experimentation, he developed an innersole of microcellular rubber that would help prevent destructive ulcers. John Girling, a wandering Englishman looking for a challenge, stopped by. He helped Dr. Brand develop "rocker" shoes and boots in which the foot rocked instead of bending on a central pivot. They proved to be feet-savers for many patients.

Dr. Brand pressed ahead. Under his direction, records of reconstruction of hands and feet passed the 5,000 mark. Medical experts heard of the many "miracles." They came to see and went away convinced. From Dr. Brand many learned new and improved methods of helping people who had suffered paralysis from damaged nerves as a result of accidents.

The now celebrated medical missionary accepted numerous honors in quiet humility. Once his wife (by this time a distinguished authority in her own field of opthalmology) found a crumpled letter in a trousers pocket. It was a notification that Dr. Brand was to receive a coveted decoration from Queen Elizabeth II, and he had not said a word about it.

Both in India and in other countries where he lectured, Dr. Paul Brand delighted in sharing his techniques with fellow medical missionaries. With them, as with the 1969 Wheaton International Conference on Missionary Medicine, he confided the purpose of his life: "Expressing the life and love of Jesus Christ while seeking to restore some of the harmony, beauty and health that is the will of God."

At Wheaton, Dr. Brand illustrated the results of this purpose. "This boy named John lost his fingers and one eye. His other eye was saved in an operation by my wife. His face was still partly paralyzed, leaving him with a peculiar half-winking leer. He looked even stranger when he smiled. He had become bitter and was a problem boy.

"He became a Christian and requested baptism. We asked the evangelical church in Vellore if they would accept him. They did. I watched him enter the church nervously for his first communion service. When he stopped beside a bench, a healthy man sitting there smiled and moved up to make a place. John sat down at peace, transformed by that simple act of acceptance. Today, he has a good factory job and is an inspiration to all his friends."

And Dr. Brand's mother, now 93?

"The last time I saw her," he said, "I had to climb four thousand feet on foot over rocks to reach her mountain hut. She's too lame to walk, so she rides horseback from village to village spreading the Good News and helping whoever she can. Her Lord and her people are her whole life. She's happy in her mission as I am happy."

The distinguished surgeon paused and looked over his audience, some of whom were medical students and young doctors contemplating Christian service abroad. "Commitment is the first step," he declared. "Not until we are in the Army of God will we know what His order of the day will be."

14.

MAP's Man of Mercy

J. RAYMOND KNIGHTON

A missionary doctor in Guatemala is in desperate need of protein-building vitamins for poverty-stricken Indians suffering from acute malnutrition. A corporation wants to donate 55,000 cases of Metrecal for hungry people overseas in return for a tax credit. A Missouri medical student wants to serve three months in an African mission hospital "to get an on-the-scene perspective of what missionary medicine is like." A Texas dentist will pay his own travel expenses for a mercy visit to a needy country. A small town M.D. in Wisconsin is under orders from his wife to "get rid of that motorcycle before you kill yourself."

Each sought help from Medical Assistance Programs (MAP), the combination drug store and medical personnel agency that serves the world.

"MAP is an idea as old as Christianity," explains J. Raymond Knighton, the dark-haired president of the Illinois mercy organization that sent over $15 million worth of medicines and medical equipment to over 1,000 medical missionaries in 81 developing countries during 1970. "It was outlined first in the parable of the Good Samaritan. MAP acts as middleman between those who can help and those who need help, coordinating supply with need so that the greatest amount of assistance reaches the areas of greatest need."

J. Raymond Knighton is a big man (6'2", 250 pounds) whose speech bespeaks his hurry, and who calls himself "a beggar for the sick." He thumbs through a folder of addresses. "Those who can help are American drug companies, manufacturers of medical equipment and supplies, physicians, dentists, and humanitarians of all vocations. Those who need help are medical missionaries and others who serve God and humanity by alleviating suffering. They are in places where they can't get a prescription filled at the corner drugstore. But we can help them here."

He quickly notes that the doctor in Guatemala received a shipment of free therapeutic vitamins, halazone, and chewable vitamins. The 55,000 cases of Metrecal were unloaded in MAP's bulging warehouse, then dispatched to Africa as a diet supplement for starving children. The Missouri medical student went to Uganda where his "concepts of medical missions were changed significantly" and he received a "much greater sense of world need." The Texas dentist was teamed with a lab technician and sent to the Indian Ocean island nation of Malagasy where they made 500 extractions and constructed 75 different prosthetic appliances in thirty days.

And the motorcycle?

"We took that, too," Knighton says with a grin. "We offered it to the medical missionary who could write the best thank-you letter to a donor during the next three months."

A visit to MAP's gleaming new offices and bulging warehouse (44,000 square feet) in the western Chicago suburb of Carol Stream, Illinois, is an eye-opener to one of the world's best exercises of compassion. You stand beside Ray Knighton and watch the loading and unloading of crates of medicines and medical supplies. You hear him say, "We're a way station, not a storage facility. The sooner we can move these medicines out, the more lives will be saved."

Knighton escorts you between stacks of packaged drugs ready for shipment. "Here's some penthrane given by Abbott Labs and going to a hospital in Ecuador. A general anesthetic agent for surgeons. This bicillin from Wyeth Labs will help fight infections in East Pakistan. Here's some Kaopectate from Upjohn that will help control infant diarrhea in Costa Rica. And this is a portion of 5,000 cases of Anacin which just came in from Whitehall Labs. Going to the Presbyterians in Korea."

A warehouse helper moves up with a truckload of drums. You read the label: Sanimaster. "Servicemaster gave this for cleaning hospital wards. The president of the company just happens to be my Sunday school teacher."

Negro minister Rev. Carlton Arthurs helps pack another shipment of Medical Assistance Programs' (MAP) medicine. From this warehouse in 1970 over $15 million of donated medicine went to over 1,000 medical missionaries in 81 countries. (MAP photo)

Pharmacist John Street, administrative assistant Beth Knighton, and technician Morell Dixon watch the manufacture of aspirin in the MAP building. (MAP photo)

Assistant Secretary of State for Dominican Republic (r) decorates MAP president, J. Raymond Knighton, in presence of coordinator Howard Shoemake (l) and Dr. Ralph Blocksma, MAP board chairman. (MAP photo)

MAP's President J. Raymond Knighton presents memberships in the International Fellowship of Medical Assistance Programs to two officials of the American Medical Association: Dr. V. T. DeVault (r), director of the AMA's Office of International Health, and Leo E. Brown, assistant to the executive vice-president of the AMA. (MAP photo)

Rat poison was dispatched by MAP to prevent an epidemic in the Dominican Republic. (MAP photo)

Dr. Bill Wallace at Methodist Hospital in Ganta, Liberia, dispenses MAP medicine. (MAP photo)

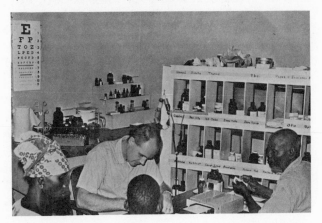

Knighton quickly checks through a stack of labels. "Material going to fifteen different denominations in twelve countries today. There's nothing sectarian about medicine," he chuckles.

He escorts you to the production department. There you meet Don Stillwell, MAP's pharmacist. "From ingredients we purchase," he says, "we're making a million tablets a week for tuberculosis, worm control, and fevers. We hope to be turning out ten million a week soon. But that won't meet the demand."

MAP's president continues showing you around. He points out a box of tapes and medical journals. "Helps the missionary doctors keep up with advances back home," he notes. At the corner of an aisle he shows off "our museum." "We're holding these old instruments and machines for doctors who request them. This old x-ray machine given to us by a clinic in Minnesota is needed somewhere."

Out of the corner of your eye you spot a workman with head bowed over a package. Sleeping? "No," Knighton says. "He's praying for the people who will be helped by the medicines in that box."

As you move toward the offices, a question forms in your mind. What about thieves and drug addicts who might try to break in? "This place is crisscrossed with radar," Knighton declares. "Anyone moving about at night will trip an alarm that sounds in the police station and in my home."

Walking towards Knighton's corner office, you pass a bevy of secretaries. "We have twenty-six full-time and seventeen part-time workers," the boss man indicates. "All on an operating budget of only $248,000 last year.* Then local groups of volunteer church women come in when we need extra help."

Now in his corner office from which you can look across the street to a Bible publisher, Knighton details how MAP operates. "We're nonprofit, nonsectarian, and under the control of twelve doctors, all outstanding doctors and Christian laymen. Our present chairman is Dr. Ralph Blocksma, a plastic surgeon in Grand Rapids, Michigan, and former medical missionary.

"For $100 we can move out two tons of medicines. For $50 we can manufacture 200,000 tablets. For $20 we can provide vitamins for a hundred infants for a year." MAP's president

---

*Of this amount, $170,000 come from handling charges paid by recipient missions, $68,000 from individual donors, and $10,000 from foundations.

stops and smiles. "I'm giving you some of our new fund-raising propaganda. But it's true."

Under questioning, Knighton confesses that "we are less effective in fund-raising than in moving medicines to places of need. We're hoping our new publications director, David Enlow, will get our message out to people who can help. *Reader's Digest* brought out an article on us in April 1971.

"We've been working under the assumption that we don't care who gets the credit, so long as the work gets done. This is great, but I've visited mission hospitals where some of the personnel didn't know where their free medicines were coming from.

"However, we will continue to fill orders from any Protestant medical missionary or mission hospital for medicines available. The only requirement is that they pay the ocean freight, unless U.S. AID comes to the rescue and foots the bill, and write a thank-you letter to the corporate or individual donor."

Knighton is particularly anxious to acquaint the public with MAP's seven-point service ministry that goes astonishingly far beyond shipping drugs overseas:

—The Supply Service gathers and distributes medicines and donated medical equipment to overseas missionary doctors and hospitals.

—The Purchasing Service buys new instruments and equipment for missionary doctors and hospitals at the lowest possible prices.

—The Student Placement Service sends senior medical students (fifty in 1969) to serve overseas with missionary doctors for three-month terms. MAP pays three-fourths of their travel expenses from the port of embarkation. Many later return as full-time medical missionaries. A recent grant from the DeWitt Wallace International Fellowship provides a program of grants-in-aid for selected medical students to obtain on-the-field experience in missionary medicine.

—The Disaster Service dispatches voluntary medical personnel and medicines to an overseas disaster area upon special request.

—The Personnel Service sends doctors and other medical and paramedical personnel on specialty short-term assignments and as vacation replacements for regular medical missionaries. Short-termers pay their own travel expenses, which are tax-deductible when routed through MAP.

—The Development Service contributes money, equipment, and supplies to medical institutions all over the world to enable them to set up modern medical facilities where none would exist otherwise.

—The Educational Service sponsors Christian medical conferences where missionary doctors discuss latest techniques and share their experiences and insights into mutual problems. Conferences recently sponsored by MAP in Western Africa and Latin America were firsts for these regions. Every three years MAP sponsors an International Conference on Missionary Medicine attended by furloughing missionaries, students interested in missionary medicine, and representatives of mission boards. The next such conference will be March 18-22, 1972, at Wheaton College.

"We manage to stay busy and keep moving," Knighton says. "We know what the ministry of medicine will do for sick and starving people. And we know how missionary medicine opens hearts and even nations to the gospel."

Knighton keeps no record of his own globe-girdling travels, but he believes he is starting on his "second million miles by plane, jeep, burro, and on foot." Twice in 1969 he flew to Afghanistan where MAP operates a rural hospital in cooperation with the Afghan government.

He is "not much of a tourist," and will go to see an attraction only "if it is near a hospital I am visiting." Though he has been to India five times, he has never seen the Taj Mahal. "When I can take Beth with me, then I'll see all the famous places," he says.

Beth Knighton, a slim, vivacious brunette, is the mother of four children. She now occupies the office of vice president, next door to her husband. "My right hand," Ray Knighton says. His "left hand," executive secretary Amy Anderson, is in the other adjoining office. She "works seventy hours a week, and she'd make it more, if I would let her."

MAP's president is "Ray" to his friends who are mostly doctors. He seldom mentions the honorary doctorate awarded him by Seattle Pacific College in 1964, nor that he was the American Medical Association's "Co-layman of the year" for 1970, nor that his academic background lies in music.

While he was only a teenager, Ray sang baritone solos in the First Nazarene Church choir in his native Chicago. Intent on a career in teaching church music, he earned Bachelor of

Music (American Conservatory of Music) and Master of Music (Michigan State University) degrees in musicology. Along the way he enlisted his pastor's daughter, Beth Reed, in a two-part harmony for life. The young couple helped pay living expenses by singing and playing the organ at funerals—up to five a day.

After a three-year stint as head of the music department for Northwest Nazarene College in Idaho, Ray returned with Beth to Chicago for graduate study. Ray was only six months away from his doctorate in musicology at Roosevelt University in Chicago when a fellow churchman suggested a change of plans.

Dr. Howard Hamlin was in their home for a routine examination of their second child, David. "Have you ever thought of working with doctors?" he suddenly asked.

Both Ray and Beth looked blank.

"I'm talking about the Christian Medical Society," Dr. Hamlin continued. "It was started by an ophthalmologist, Dr. Kenneth Gieser, about ten years ago. We've got big plans to organize chapters of Christian doctors, dentists, and students all over the country. We need a director."

Ray laughed. "About all I know in the medical line is to take aspirins for a headache."

"But you know how to deal with people," Dr. Hamlin said seriously. "I've seen you direct choirs. Doctors are people, too."

At Dr. Hamlin's urging, Ray met with the CMS board. He took the job, and CMS chapters began springing up from Boston to San Francisco. Chapter members began helping medical missionaries on an individual basis. Some gave free time to clinics in downtown missions and other needy institutions. Under Ray's counsel some of the students and younger doctors became medical missionaries.

One of CMS's best pastor friends was the late Dr. Donald Barnhouse of Philadelphia. A drug executive member mentioned that his company was going to discard $25,000 worth of drugs and wondered if the pastor knew any place they could be used.

"Send them to Ray Knighton," Dr. Barnhouse suggested. "He knows every Christian doctor in the world."

Ray did not hear about the shipment until it had already been shipped. It required all his ingenuity to find a place to put it. When the drugs arrived, he had the CMS office girls move their typewriters and desks into the hall. Then he unloaded the drugs from the delivery truck and stacked them in the office.

That first drug donation (sent to Ethiopia) marked the beginning of a significant new CMS service as Ray began discovering other companies and individuals willing to donate medicines and supplies to overseas mission doctors.

Two years later Ray and the CMS board decided to call the new service "Medico." But just before ordering letterheads, Ray learned that Dr. Tom Dooley had taken this name for his organization. The Board switched to Missionary Assistance Programs, then changed "missionary" to "medical" because "this might help us get into places where missionaries aren't allowed."

At first MAP provided drugs and medical supplies to CMS members only. But the program grew and broadened until, in 1965, MAP became an independent organization. Under Ray Knighton's leadership, MAP has increased the dollar value of medical supplies sent overseas thirty times over.

While Ray covers the map for MAP, Beth keeps home operations running smoothly. All four Knighton children have a vital interest in medicine.

Nancye, a registered nurse, the eldest and a graduate of Wheaton College, was recently married to Bradford Jones, a former co-worker with the Billy Graham Team.

David is a senior premed student at Wheaton College, where he was president of the Student Missionary Fellowship and sports information director for the college. He has served one term abroad in Africa's Ivory Coast. While in Africa, he helped deliver babies and perform major surgery, did cancer research for famed British physician Dr. Dennis Burkitt, and saw how vital MAP shipments were to one mission hospital. "When MAP medicine doesn't come," he wrote home, "they almost have to close up."

Tom, a high school senior, plans a career in plastic surgery. He served one term abroad with MAP's program in the Dominican Republic.

Mike, the youngest and a sixth grader, is interested in science, and helps around the MAP warehouse during free time.

Ray is "too busy for golf, but not for a family 'sing' around the piano." When he arrives home from an overseas trip, the younger boys—especially Mike—can never hear enough of daddy's adventures.

Does MAP's president regret giving up a musical career? "No," he says, "but I'd be untruthful to say I don't love music.

I sing for missionaries when they'll let me and I love to hear great choirs. But I think the sweetest music I ever heard was down in rural Haiti at a mission hospital for children. We had just finished dinner when suddenly I heard their little voices blending in a hymn. I knew that they were able to sing because of the hospital and the medicine we had sent."

15.

Never Too Old for the Congo

MARTIN ERICSSON, M.D.

The Swedish mother nudged her spellbound young son. "Your food's getting cold, Martin."

But young Martin Ericsson was hardly interested in food. Fork in hand, he sat captivated by the missionary's dramatic stories of the exotic Congo. He imagined himself in pith helmet and shorts, doctor's bag in hand, tending the wounds of a man whose arm had been ripped by a wild animal. He saw tattooed dancers clad only in leopard skins cavorting in a circle to the beat of drums.

Fifty years later, in 1962, Dr. Martin Ericsson stepped off a plane in torrid Léopoldville and saw his boyhood dream fulfilled —at least for a few months.

He was there under the Congo Protestant Relief Agency's "Operation Doctor," an organization formed a few months before to bring medicine and spiritual help to the newly independent nation. The undeveloped Congo was huge, six times the size of California and third largest nation in Africa. Hundreds of Belgian physicians had fled from the chaos engulfing the country, leaving it frightfully deficient in medical services.

Dr. Ericsson was assigned to fill in for then unknown Dr. Paul Carlson at a bush hospital while the young missionary doctor was in Europe studying French and tropical medicine.

The two doctors had never met. When Dr. Ericsson reached Léopoldville, he knew Dr. Carlson's hospital was named Wasolo, and little else. And none of the missionaries he met seemed to know much about Wasolo, except for one who said, "The name means 'end of the world.' I've heard that when you get there it's closer home to keep on going."

Dr. Ericsson kept going—to Wasolo—by plane and then by truck for the last two hundred and fifty miles. Two U.S. missionary nurses welcomed him to the 80-bed hospital, a white, one-story building on a verdant rise. "You are the only doctor for a hundred thousand people," one of them told him. "We've been waiting for you."

The hospital's sole source of electricity was an erratic light plant. There were few medicines, and a constant overflow of patients. There was little money. Before independence in 1960, the Belgians had contributed $500 a month for staff salaries, maintenance, and medicine, but under Congolese rule, this had dropped to $20 a month.

Diagnosis required the patience of Job. The people had almost no understanding of hygiene, sanitation, contagious diseases, or body functions. Pain was to the Congolese a *nyama* (animal) inside. Most patients claimed, whether or not it was true, that they hurt all over, just to persuade Dr. Ericsson that they were *mpasi mingi mpenia* (very sick).

From sunrise until late evening, and often in between then and the next sunrise, he treated and operated by the light of a kerosene lamp when the unpredictable light plant refused to work. The sight of a steady parade of mothers arriving after a journey of two days with their slaty-gray, dehydrating babies was heartrending. The doctor knew that many of these babies would die within hours unless they were given transfusions of life-giving fluids. And more often than not the hospital didn't have them. Almost as heartbreaking were the women who had been in labor for two and three days, carried in on crude blanket stretchers by trotting men.

Dr. Ericsson left in December 1962, when another short-term doctor arrived. The African staff sang and prayed and begged him to return. "Dr. Paul needs you and we need you," an elder intoned. "You are older than he and have much wisdom."

Back in Cedar Falls, Iowa, where he was a general practitioner, Dr. Ericsson celebrated his sixtieth birthday. "This trip proved to me that I'm not too old to be a medical missionary," he told his wife. "I'm going back."

Martha Ericsson looked lovingly at her balding husband. His roundish head was rimmed with a fringe of gray. "Stubborn

Swede," she murmured. "We'll go together. This is what you have wanted to do as long as I have known you."

Indeed, the series of short-term jaunts to the Congo which Martin Ericsson began in 1962 was the fulfillment of a lifetime dream for the Swedish doctor. Ever since he could remember, Martin had wanted to follow in the footsteps of his hero, Dr. David Livingstone. But college and medical school were far too expensive for his father's modest income as a factory foreman in the old country.

When Martin was seventeen, two of his older brothers came home from the United States for a visit. Martin went back with them, although the only English he knew when he arrived in America was how to count to ten.

Like many other Scandinavian immigrants, he sought work in the sawmills and mines of northern Minnesota. When the iron mine where he had been working shut down, he drifted to Spokane, Washington, where one of his brothers was a minister. The older brother advised him to "get an education before it's too late."

At twenty, Martin started high school at Bethel Academy in St. Paul, Minnesota, a school sponsored by the (Swedish) Baptist General Conference. He earned his diploma in three years. Then he enrolled at the University of Minnesota in Minneapolis, where he joined the student volunteers and regained the hope of becoming a medical missionary.

Finally, at thirty-two, having received his M.D. from the University of Minnesota Medical School, he began interning at St. Mary's Hospital in Minneapolis. But the Great Depression had fallen upon America. Instead of sending new missionaries, mission boards were hard pressed to maintain support of those already on the field.

Martin had borrowed heavily to complete medical school, so he jumped at the opportunity to work temporarily with an older doctor in Long Prairie, Minnesota, a small town northwest of Minneapolis, while the man's doctor son was away doing post-graduate work.

Seven months later, when the young doctor returned to Long Prairie, Dr. Ericsson moved to Chicago. There he secured employment with an insurance company while getting additional training. And he stayed long enough in Chicago to win the love of a blue-eyed brunette Swedish-American girl named Martha Anderson.

Shortly after their wedding, Dr. Ericsson received two un-expected letters prompted by similar tragedies. One was from the American Baptist Foreign Mission Society asking if he could replace a missionary doctor in India who had been killed in an automobile accident. In reply, Dr. Ericsson sent his regrets, explaining that he felt honor-bound to pay off his debts before embarking on a missionary career. The second letter came from the elderly doctor in Long Prairie, Minnesota. His son had been killed in an automobile accident; would Dr. Ericsson come back and join him as a permanent partner?

In Long Prairie, the Ericssons were greeted warmly by the citizenry. Only the young girls of marriageable age who had known the doctor as an eligible bachelor were disappointed.

During five happy years in northwest Minnesota, Dr. Ericsson filled the role of an old-fashioned family doctor. In an area where many Scandinavian immigrants lived, his accent was an advantage. Town and country folk came to trust the strong-shouldered man who was willing to ride on hayracks in mid-winter, below-zero weather and sit the night through beside a sick child or a woman in labor.

In 1941 a relative encouraged him to come to Cedar Falls, Iowa, and take over the practice of a retired M.D. He came. Two years later he volunteered for Army service. Mustered out in 1943 with captain's rank, he resumed practice, thinking that at forty-one he was too old to become a medical missionary.

The Ericssons joined the First Baptist Church and moved into the life of the bustling Midwestern community. Both accepted Sunday school classes. Dr. Ericsson was elected Sunday school superintendent, a post he held for sixteen consecutive years. They entertained missionaries in their homes and gave financial support to overseas work.

The years slipped by. Daughter Karen was born. Their oldest son was killed in an automobile accident.

Dr. Ericsson's practice grew and he brought in a junior partner, then a third and a fourth and a fifth—all Christian doctors. As Cedar Falls Medical Associates, they built one of the largest medical practices in Iowa.

By 1962, when Dr. Ericsson was fifty-nine, he was delivering second generation babies and friends were teasing him about disappearing hair. Sometimes he and his associates talked about short-term service on the mission field. They decided that if one of them should go, the group would continue to pay him a salary.

The problems of the Congo following independence began making news. Dr. Ericsson read about the drastic need for doctors, in the face of the Belgian departure. He said to his wife, "I wonder if there's a way an old man could help."

A few days later Dr. Oliver Hasselblad, director of the American Leprosy Mission, spoke at the First Baptist Church. Dr. Ericsson confided to Dr. Hasselblad his concern for the Congo. Dr. Hasselblad gave him the address of the Congo Protestant Relief Agency in New York and suggested he inquire about their Operation Doctor program. Their reply delighted him. Learning that he was not too old for short-term service set Dr. Ericsson into immediate action. Upon receipt of his application, the CPRA assigned him to serve four months at Dr. Paul Carlson's hospital, Wasolo.

After returning from that assignment, he applied for a second short term in the Congo. He and Mrs. Ericsson arrived back in January 1964, just as the threatening storm of civil violence was building to a peak. But this time the CPRA leaders felt he should serve at the Baptist Mission in Pimu where there was a 75-bed hospital and no doctor.

Except for being less isolated, Pimu was Wasolo all over again. The beds were always full, and the overflow patients had to sleep in the aisles. Some days Dr. Ericsson could not keep count of the number of operations. With public health care nonexistent, whooping cough, tetanus, measles, amoebic dysentery, leprosy, and malaria ravaged villages in the politically unstable area around the hospital.

As summer advanced, marauding bands of agitators moved into the area. When the hospital exhausted its supply of penicillin and aspirin, Dr. Ericsson sent an emergency message to his associates. They air-mailed back a shipment of medicines.

Communist Chinese agitators were convincing rebel soldiers that all whites, especially American missionaries, were their enemies and should be killed. Congolese said they could no longer assume the responsibility for protection and warned the Ericssons, the English nurse, and the English evangelist and his wife who made up the foreign staff that they should leave.

On August 4, Stanleyville fell to the rebels. The Ericssons and the English nurse made up their minds to go. The English evangelist and his wife said they would stay.

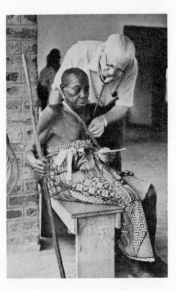

Dr. Martin Ericsson examines patient at Wasolo (meaning "the end of the world"), The Congo. Dr. Paul Carlson served here before his martyrdom.

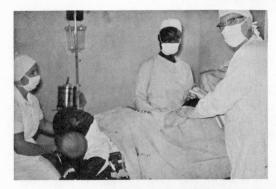

Dr. Ericsson in the operating room.

Ambulance service in the Congo.

Four days later the rebels overran the station and ransacked the missionaries' homes. They found the English couple hiding under beds but, because of their nationality, did not harm them.

Twenty-eight missionaries were killed during the last months of 1964. One was Dr. Paul Carlson, arrested at Wasolo, and shot down in Stanleyville as he attempted to escape.

Friends of the Ericssons welcomed them back to Cedar Falls with gratitude. From area service clubs and churches there came a flood of speaking requests. Dr. Ericsson showed pictures and related experiences that brought tears to many eyes and donations of all sizes. The monies were sent to the Congo Protestant Relief Agency and Medical Assistance Programs (MAP). MAP, Dr. Ericsson explained, was the main supplier of medicines for mission hospitals in the Congo.

To those who said "Of course, you're not going back to the Congo after all this killing," he replied cheerily. "I'm ready to return as soon as possible."

He did not have to wait long.

In 1966 the Evangelical Free Church asked Dr. Ericsson to help a young missionary doctor at their Tandala station in the Congo. Backed up by his partners, he and Mrs. Ericsson agreed to go for nine months.

The staff was larger at this 110-bed hospital than at Wasolo or Pimu, but Dr. Ericsson worked untiringly. When his younger colleague or one of the missionary nurses would show concern, he would reply, "Don't worry about me. There's still a lot of spark left in the old engine."

Two weeks before the Ericssons were scheduled to leave, about thirty village chiefs came to beg him to stay. He tried to explain about his work in Iowa and the children at home. But they pressed him further. Finally he said, "I never make a decision apart from my wife." At this the chief dispatched a delegation to see Mrs. Ericsson.

When the Ericssons boarded the little mission plane at the airstrip near the station, one of the chiefs stepped out of a crowd of five hundred and said, "We'll give you three months vacation. Then you must come back."

As the plane taxied for a takeoff, the Ericssons were waving to the crying people. "After this," Dr. Ericsson told his wife, "it's going to be awfully hard for me to show sympathy to a neurotic back home."

Back in Cedar Falls, Dr. Ericsson received more invitations

to speak and show pictures of his work, as did one of his associates who had just returned from short-term service in Lebanon. And another doctor from their group was leaving for several months in East Pakistan with the assurance of financial support from his partners.

Now sixty-seven, Dr. Ericsson is eager to go out for the fourth time. Asked when, he said, "Soon as I can find somebody to take my place. We can't all leave Cedar Falls. Some of us must stay behind and take care of our patients."

Too old? "Certainly not," he declared. "Because of my experience as a small town and country doctor, I'm better adjusted to mission hospitals than these young fellows coming out of medical schools and trained to use their fancy instruments. Out there in the Congo and other needy places, what the people need most is a doctor who specializes in the skin and what's under it—a general practitioner who loves God and people."

And that's what Dr. Martin Ericsson is.

16.

Medical Missions in the Seventies

The medical missionary of a century ago had a taxing but simple program: Keep his preaching and teaching colleagues (the elite corps) in good health* and treat and convert the sick who came to his one-man dispensary. He had few medicines from which to choose, no journals to read, and in most places few government officials to placate. But this is not to discount his heroism and sacrifice in those pre-penicillin days when medicine and equipment from home required months for delivery.

Now in a rapidly changing world where the Early Bird is a satellite, not a rooster, the medical missionary faces a plethora of challenging questions.

—Should I spend two hours in surgery helping one man or should I use that time to inoculate one hundred?

—Should I limit my hospital beds to twenty-five patients where I can build witnessing relations or should I bring in a hundred and spend less time with each in spiritual conversation?

—Should I view the nearby government hospital as an ally or a competitor?

—How much should our mission budget be for a medical

---

*A few missionary doctors still serve in this support capacity. For example, Dr. Douglas Swanson is the doctor-on-call for some 200 Wycliffe Bible Translators at Wycliffe's jungle base in Peru, base national employees, and Indian teachers and their families.

program to fight malnutrition and how much for an agricultural program that helps prevent malnutrition?

—Should we, in view of the population explosion, emphasize family planning more than saving the lives of old people?

—To build a better relationship with the government, should I turn the hospital directorship over to a national whom I know is not fully qualified?

—Should I resign from the mission and take a job with a foundation or private hospital where I will have better equipment and a larger salary but will have less freedom to propagate my faith?

Reasons for finding new strategies in medical missions are not hard to find.

Rising nationalism demands that the foreign missionary be a servant of the national church. The traditional "Great White Father" role is no longer accepted in most situations.

Colonial European governments placed few restrictions on their citizen-missionaries serving God among their faraway, exotic subjects. Indeed, the missionaries were frequently considered a part of the colonial team. Now, new national governments in Asia, Africa, and Latin America are imposing limitations and demands on medical practice. Control by foreigners is out and service *under* nationals is in.

In addition, the missionary doctor is no longer the only means of medical help in developing countries. There are nonreligious doctors and paramedical personnel sent by foreign governments (sometimes Russian and Chinese), foundations, and corporations. There are also national professionals who may have more advanced training than the missionaries. Governments are building new hospitals and funding national health programs while many missionary medics must limp along with decadent buildings and outmoded or insufficient equipment.

Missionaries, both medical and otherwise, have themselves helped bring about these changes. Missionaries taught most of the present government leaders in the new black African countries. They trained national physicians and nurses. They convinced people that leprosy and tuberculosis and malaria can be controlled. They led people to expect hospital care when they are sick.

Furthermore, the missionary doctor, in contrast to his colleagues in hospitals at home, holds no special position of prestige. He is "one of the troops" in his own mission. His colleagues on the field may be nurses, medical technologists, business administrators, all on the same salary scale as himself. They recognize his specialized skills, but they look upon him more as a fellow-worker than as a superior.

The future of medical missions ranked high on the agenda of two recent top-level conventions: the Third Conference on International Health sponsored by the American Medical Association and the Fifth International Conference on Missionary Medicine sponsored by Medical Assistance Programs.

The medical directors of the United Methodist, Presbyterian U.S.A., and Southern Baptist foreign mission boards addressed this challenge at a seminar during the AMA Conference.

Dr. Franklin Fowler, medical director for Southern Baptist's overseas ministries, emphasized the uniqueness of Christian missions and stated the objectives of the Southern Baptist medical effort overseas: "To provide medical assistance to people in foreign countries as an expression of Christian love and as a means of witness in order that they may be brought to God through Jesus Christ."

A veteran medical missionary himself, Dr. Fowler noted that overseas medicine is becoming more specialized and more expensive. "Whether we like it or not," he said, "we must live with the fact that overseas doctors are interested in specialization. We have imported this trend ourselves. And equipment that once was a rarity is now needed for the foreign hospitals—the cobalt intensifier, for example."

Dr. Fowler cited the increase of government concern for health which "must figure into the plans of church-related medical ministries. The medical missionaries no longer hold a monopoly on modern medicine. The ambassador to Paraguay told me this afternoon that seven years ago there were only seven health centers outside of his country's capital. Today there are sixty. Now and in the future, medical missionaries will find themselves competing with national private physicians and government institutions."

Dr. Fowler acknowledged that he could only generalize in looking to the future "because countries have different backgrounds and cultures and are at different levels in development." The Southern Baptist leader did, however, see "major trends" toward more participation in training nationals, increased activity in community health, and increasing nationalism.

He expressed hope that the day will come "when we can

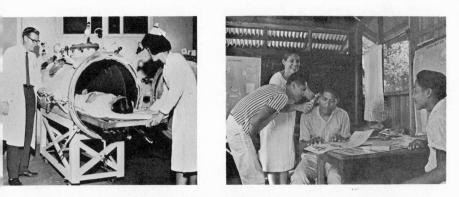

Left: Foreign hospitals are demanding expensive emergency equipment. Dr. Charles G. Tabor at Wallace Memorial Baptist Hospital made the first barometric 02 tank in Korea himself. (Southern Baptist Foreign Mission Board photo) **Right:** Training of national health workers will gain more importance in the '70s. R.N. Joan Lempke of Wycliffe Bible Translators in Peru trains Amazonian Indian *sanitarios* who will return to their tribes and operate modest clinics. (Wycliffe Bible Translators photo)

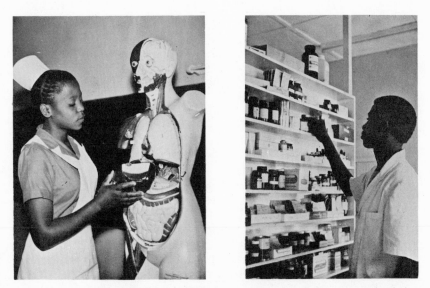

Left: Swaziland nurse studies anatomy at Nazarene Nursing College. (Church of the Nazarene photo) **Right:** African pharmacist trained by the Sudan Interior Mission in Nigeria. (MAP photo)

The International Convention on Missionary Medicine brings together medical missionaries and students from around the globe. Here a panel of missionary doctors and nurses, chaired by J. Raymond Knighton of MAP (c), discusses at the 1968 ICMM the topic "How Changing Methods Influence Physician-Nurse Relationships." Next ICMM conference sponsored by MAP will be held in the spring of 1972 on the Wheaton College campus, Wheaton, Illinois. (MAP photo)

send medical missionary physicians to teach in national medical schools where they will have unique opportunities for witness to students." He saw an increased need for more and better nursing schools and institutions, for training laboratory and X-ray technicians, anesthetists, midwives, national chaplains, and hospital administrators.

He foresaw the community health approach as "following the example of Christ, who did His work in the villages where the people lived," but he did not think that the traditional emphasis on the value of the individual would be lost in such an approach.

Finally, predicting "more and more nationalism," he added, "I was very pleased to be in Nigeria last month at an official meeting where the proprietorship of five of our mission hospitals was turned over to the Nigerian Baptist Convention. This has already happened for us in Japan and Brazil," he said. "More and more we are realizing that we foreign missionaries are guests in the countries where we serve."

Dr. Theodore T. Stevenson, representing the United Presbyterian Church at the AMA meeting, agreed with Dr. Fowler

on the need to push training programs for nurses, lab technicians, and other paramedical personnel. "Every hospital," he
said, "should be a place where someone is trained."

But, Dr. Stevenson stressed, the idea that mission hospitals
should be at the level of hospitals in the United States is being
challenged today. "One of our doctors made a study recently
in Korea and found our hospitals there to be better equipped
than ever, but rising costs were making it difficult for many
patients to afford the care. The study showed that some patients
were even having to sell farm animals to pay their bills. We are
wondering if we should keep on developing sophisticated hospitals overseas with patient costs above the economic level of
many nationals."

The Presbyterian leader felt that Christian missions "should
consider more cooperation with governments. It is my experience
that governments pay little attention to church hospitals. Yet
a few years ago the government of India discovered in a family
planning conference attended by over three hundred hospital administrators that 20 percent of the hospital beds in the country
were in church-related hospitals."

As an example of cooperation, he cited the Presbyterian hospital in Meshed, Iran, the holiest Muslim city in Iran and only
fifty miles from the Russian border, "where we sought opportunity to work with the government. The University of Meshed
uses our hospital for teaching. They supplement our staff. We
continue to run the hospital as we wish without restrictions
on our programs."

Dr. Reeve H. Beets from the Board of Missions of the United
Methodist Church concurred with his Presbyterian counter-
part as to the necessity for cooperating with governments. "Medical education is getting too expensive for individual churches
or a group of churches together to finance," he said. "A wonderful way of cooperation is for the government to provide the
money and the missions to supply the personnel." And he added,
"I would be very happy if some of our missionaries would want
to go to work in a government hospital."

The Methodist leader agreed with the others in expecting
"rising nationalism to be an important factor in the future.
The time has gone," he declared, "when Westerners can go over
and tell people of other countries what they should do." Re-
ferring to the medical agency of the World Council of Churches,
he said, "The reason the Christian Medical Commission with

headquarters in Geneva, Switzerland, has such excellent prospects is that most of its members are non-Westerners."

And Dr. Beets predicted "some shifting of church-related medical work into preventive medicine and public health." But he added, "I hope this will be done by nationals who have been trained in church-related institutions."

Dr. James McGilvray, director of the World Council's Christian Medical Commission, was more blunt than the denominational leaders in speaking to the AMA conference. He indicated that "setting up a hospital-centered approach to health care in developing countries may have been a mistake. It would be ridiculous to suggest that hospitals are not a necessary component of health care, but in making them a pivot of a . . . system we have successfully given the impression that the episodic treatment of patients is the major emphasis in our concern for the health of all people."

After pointing out that 95 percent of the churches' medical missions resources have gone into "institutionalized curative programs," he called the system "particularly irrational when applied to economically disadvantaged people. An increase in hospital beds will not solve the formidable problems in India where the bulk of the population are victims of poverty, infectious diseases, and malnutrition. What is really required is not more beds and expensive buildings to house them, but a rationalization of existing facilities and a rapid expansion of middle-level health workers."

A second dilemma of medical mission strategists, he declared, is "insufficient manpower." There must not only be more medical and paramedical personnel, but to establish a viable system new ways of utilizing and training health workers must be found. He suggested the "team approach" to medicine as one way which might bring health care to all.

He continued, "A third dilemma lies in the interface between what we know about disease and what we have yet to learn about the delivery of health care. . . . If we were to take 10 percent of the brain power and finance which now goes into clinical and biomedical research and apply it to research in health care delivery systems, we could effect a revolution in international health. . . . Such research would seek to tailor health care to the economic limitations under which people live.

"We know most of the causes [of disease] are attributable to community situations—traditions which exist in homes, together with environmental factors in the community. Any rational approach to health care planning would therefore start from there if it is to have any effective influence on the patterns of disease."

The Fifth International Conference on Missionary Medicine sponsored by Medical Assistance Programs (MAP) emphasized the spiritual work of the medical missionary. With representatives of both denominational and faith missions attending, this conference emphasized the relationship between medical missions and Christian evangelism.

Dr. Donald A. McGavran, director of the Department of World Missions at Fuller Theological Seminary, placed medicine within the orbit of other missionary ministries, "all subordinate to the ultimate and overriding goal that all of God's children have a real chance to know him." The veteran missionary, best known as the "apostle of church growth," excluded from consideration "medical enterprises carried on by Christians abroad with the exclusive purpose of healing the body without spiritual work." "Such missions have little to do with church growth," he said. "Our stance in medical missions must be openly and unashamedly Christian with the desire that those we serve may know the abundant life which Christ offers," he told his audience of furloughing medical missionaries and other Christians involved in medical work at home. "Our Lord counted men's bodies important. He healed people. So do we. He regarded his cures as signs of his messiahship. We regard our healing ministries as witness to the Great Physician. He invited many of those he healed to become his followers. So do we invite those whom we heal."

Dr. McGavran, who, though not a medical doctor, administered missionary hospitals in India, challenged missionary medics to see themselves as a most important part of the Church's total mission. "You have great prestige," he said. "You serve at the point of keenly felt need. You have the respect and reverence formerly ascribed to rulers of rural society in many parts of the world, and, to whom much is given, much more shall be required. You are ambassadors, beseeching men to come to Christ. And you must rightly ask of your mission: Are we communicating the gospel as well as we can? Are we moving to reach long-range goals in church growth?"

He called for an "understanding of how churches grow abroad," and cited examples of "the great growth which God expects in terms of new converts." He mentioned as examples the Sudan Interior Mission in Ethiopia (120,000), the Christian and Missionary Alliance in West Irian (15,000), the Assembly of God in Brazil (from less than 20,000 in Brazil to the present 1,500,000).

And he suggested that missionary medics in the future "help everyone but spend most of their time with those known to be responsive."

Dr. Paul Brand emphasized to the ICMM group the spiritual life of the individual missionary medic. "Don't expect your spiritual life to be transformed on the way out or when you arrive," he advised. "The mission field will bring out what you were here. The weaknesses in your own character will be exposed."

The eminent surgeon stressed two weaknesses medical missionaries should try to overcome:

—The tendency to pride and boastfulness. "We medical missionaries find humble people willing to feed our vanity, put us on the pedestal, give answers we expect and say nothing about our mistakes. We must fight against this tendency to think we are wonderful. Pride can ruin our ministries."

—The tendency to become fatigued. "We have great demands on our time, but sometimes we must forget that people are dying and remember that as human beings we have just so much capacity for work. We cannot afford to drive ourselves to the point where we neglect our quiet times of prayer and Bible reading and become irritable to our families and colleagues."

The man who pioneered in rehabilitative surgery for leprosy victims reminded his audience of Jesus' commission to His disciples, "As my Father hath sent me, so send I you." "I feel that I am working with God as I seek to restore in my inadequate way some of the beauty, harmony, and health that is the will of God. We may not all be preachers," he said, "but we can all be expressions of the life and love of Jesus Christ.

"It isn't always necessary to heal a person for him to feel the love of God in you," he declared. "I recall the case of a blind woman who was brought to the eye hospital at Vellore by a relative. By the time my wife saw that she could not be helped, the relative had melted away. My wife reluctantly put the blind woman in a ward and gave her some eye drops. Although everyone was kind to her, this old lady complained continually and made life very difficult in her ward. Finally the relative returned and took her home as blind as she had come.

"Some time later we heard about a church where a great revival had started after forty people came from a distant village inquiring about the gospel. 'We want to know more about the Jesus God whom the doctors and nurses know in that eye hospital,' the seekers said. 'We want this God to change us the way He changed the old blind woman.'"

Dr. Brand's story perhaps best illustrates the motivation of the medical missionaries who will go forth in the seventies under the auspices of evangelical churches. They will want to go as healing witnesses for their God who can give "liberty to the captives, . . . recovery of sight to the [spiritually] blind, [and] . . . set free the oppressed." *

---

*Luke 4:18. From the Today's English Version of the New Testament. Copyright © American Bible Society 1966.

17.

Postscript: For Further Information . . .

The medical professional (doctor, nurse, medical technologist, etc.) who wants to serve abroad is best advised to contact his pastor, denominational or faith mission board, and a Christian service agency such as the Christian Medical Society (1122 Westgate, Oak Park, Illinois 60301) or Medical Assistance Programs (Box 50, Wheaton, Illinois 60187).

Many mission boards as well as CMS or MAP are able to arrange for short-term assignments for both professional personnel and students. For shorter visits (two weeks to three months) the volunteer and/or his supporting church and friends should expect to pay part or all of his travel expenses with hospitality provided by the host mission. For appointments as long as a year, travel costs may be assumed by the sponsoring organizations. Of course, these are only generalizations. Specific details can be obtained from the agency or mission board.

Much more procedure is involved in securing a long-term or career appointment. Besides meeting personal and professional qualifications, sending agencies usually require at least a year or more of Bible and theological training. There is hardly a mission board involved in overseas medicine that is not pleading for recruits. Doctors (general practitioners and qualified specialists in many fields, particularly surgery), dentists, nurses, hospital administrators and business managers, medical technologists, pharmacists, and hospital chaplains are wanted.

Students who feel God is leading them toward a career in

medical missions should seek advice from vocational counselors. One book of special interest to potential medical students is:

How Medical Students Finance Their Education. U.S. Dept. of H.E.W., Public Health Service, U.S. Government Printing Office, Division of Public Documents, Washington, D.C. 20402. A survey of medical and osteopathic students, 1963, 64, 65.

A book of interest to both students and professionals is:

Medical Care in Developing Countries. A primer on the medicine of poverty, and a symposium from Makerere Medical College, Uganda, Africa. Oxford University Press. May be ordered from the Christian Medical Society.

A book of special interest to those interested in preventive medicine abroad is:

Child Nutrition in Developing Countries, a handbook for field-workers of the Agency for International Development (AID). Order for $1.00 from the U. S. Government Printing Office, Division of Public Documents, Washington, D. C. 20402.

Two recent statistical and survey reports which are of interest to all concerned with medical missions are:

Medicine and Missions—A Survey of Medical Missions, prepared by Edward R. Dayton with the facilities of The Missions Advanced Research and Communication Center and the assistance of Medical Assistance Programs. May be ordered for $4.00 from MAP, Box 50, Wheaton, Illinois, 60187.
North American Protestant Ministries Overseas Directory. 8th edition. Missionary Research Library in cooperation with Missions Advanced Research and Communication Center, published by Word Books, Waco, Texas. Contains a listing (with addresses) of all North American Protestant missionary sending agencies, their fields, and numbers and types of workers in each field.

Also in print are many denominational mission study books that accent the ministry of medicine and inspirational biographies of outstanding medical missionaries. Biographies published by Word Books include:

Punjab Pioneer, Charles Reynolds, $4.95. The true life story of Dame Edith Brown—outstanding physician and surgeon, a pioneer in medical education for women in India, and founder of Ludhiana Christian Medical College.

Intrigue in Santo Domingo, James C. Hefley, $3.95. The book-length story of Howard Shoemake, Southern Baptist missionary and representative of Medical Assistance Programs (MAP) in the Dominican Republic. Though not a doctor, Shoemake has pioneered in meaningful medical programs that offer great potential in all developing countries.

Doctor in an Old World, Helen Thames Raley, $3.95. A dramatic recounting of the life of Dr. Robert Earl Beddoe, whose career as a medical missionary to China spanned two World Wars. Dr. Beddoe, a Southern Baptist missionary, not only established many dispensaries, hospitals, and nursing and medical schools, but he found time to think and plan a basic strategy of missions.

Himalayan Heartbeat, Ken Anderson, $3.75. The story of Dr. Geoffrey Lehman, a young English engineer turned doctor, who served a people of great need in the rugged Himalayas.

Medical Missions Scrapbook

• Four young amateur American archaeologists huddled around a campfire in the beautiful highlands of western Honduras. They had been exploring Mayan ruins that day in 1960 and were enchanted with the charm of the countryside.

The mayor of the nearby village joined them by their fire. "The tourists will be coming soon," Guy Bevel, one of the four, said to him.

The official of the poor village shook his head. "Señor, even God has forgotten that we are here. The caballos and burros are the only transportation we have."

Young Bevel, a Baptist layman and sales manager for an auto dealership, wondered if the government sent any kind of aid—like a visit from a doctor.

Again the mayor shook his head. "My people have never seen a doctor." Then he lamented again, "Even God has forgotten us."

The sad phrase haunted Bevel until he launched *Amigos*, a program in which American students gave their summers for health and community development programs in neglected villages of Central America.

In 1969, three hundred and fifty *Amigos* gave approximately a half-million inoculations. They set up educational programs, including literacy work in Spanish, English language classes, and health and hygiene programs in forty rural communities. And other *Amigo* projects have started in Los Angeles, San Francisco, Tucson, Denver, and elsewhere.

All this resulted from a poor man's wail that "God has forgotten us."

• *Refugees arriving in Hong Kong from Communist China who need medical aid are usually reluctant at first to seek help from mission hospitals. A man with a fractured limb may turn to an Oriental herbalist who for a fee applies a poultice made from herbs, animal excrement, and a large cockroach. A person ill with tuberculosis may buy antibiotics over the drugstore counter without a prescription.*
"Many come to us only after they are in real trouble," says Dr. Don Langford, a Southern Baptist doctor stationed in Hong Kong. "By this time an injured limb may have developed gangrene. Or, when we prescribe an antibiotic or steroid for them in a real emergency, chances are they have become resistant to the drug. We talk to them, of course, about their spiritual needs, but what we say means very little to them unless we back it up by what we do for them."

• Twelve years ago Mrs. Adrian Gonzalez, a Costa Rican Baptist nurse, her pastor husband, and fellow national Dr. Francisco Chavarria organized *Caravanas de Buena Voluntad* (Caravans of Good Will) to take medical help into remote corners of their country.

Now six *Caravanas* are held each year. The team includes both Baptist nationals and missionaries. One enthusiastic member is Dr. Ricardo Villalobos, a dentist who after his conversion became a deacon and Sunday school teacher. On a recent *Caravana* he pulled three hundred teeth in the shade of a tree while a colleague, Dr. Hugo Miranda, examined four hundred sick persons in a stable.

• *Dr. Lorne Brown, a Southern Baptist representative in Kenya, reports "a different approach" to medical missions. Some churches there have been setting up medical assistants or nurses in private practice. The church constructs and keeps up a clinic building and provides a Christian witness through each clinic. The medical practitioner earns his living from patient fees. He is responsible for upkeep of clinic equipment and pays the mission for all drugs obtained locally. Other drugs provided through Medical Assistance Programs (MAP) come to him free.*
Dr. Brown visits each clinic two or three times a week, per-

forms *some minor surgery, and assists with special diagnostic health.*

"*People within the communities obtain medical care not previously available to them,*" *the Southern Baptist missionary says. "The churches have a unique opportunity for evangelism. We have none of the employee-employer relationship which is so distasteful these days in Africa. These men realize that I am working for them rather than they for me.*"

• "It is clear from our experience and from a survey of the problems in any developing country that no foreign aid agency can solve the health, education, agriculture, or any other problems of a developing country solely, or even chiefly, by the direct application of foreign aid to these problems. The only strategy that gives any hope of success is to help the poor countries increase their capacity to deal with their own problems. In this connection, vigorous self-help on the part of the receiving country is crucial." (C. Tyler Wood, Special Assistant to the Administrator, U.S. Agency for International Development)

• "*A small African country decided to construct and operate a medical school with Western help and guidance. Eighteen of the first 20 graduates left the country within two years. They were not trained to serve in their own country.*" *(Spoken by Dr. E. Croft Long, Associate Dean of Medicine, Duke University and official of Project Med-Aid at the Fourth Conference on International Health, Chicago, 1969)*

• Dr. John K. Miller, a Presbyterian U. S. missionary in the Congo, has done something about kwashiorkor, the malady that befalls children dying of starvation. Upon learning that children under five have only a 50–50 chance of reaching adulthood, he laid out a plan based on three simple principles.

The first principle maintained that the foods used to combat kwashiorkor must be available and known by the people concerned.

The second held that teaching must have priority over therapy. To carry out this principle, Dr. Miller had to run herd on the hospital staff to prevent its giving vitamin pills and blood transfusions unnecessarily. Mothers had to be convinced that a faulty diet was the cause of their children's illness and that only a corrected diet—not hospital magic—could make them well again and keep them well.

The third principle contended that the program must fit the area where it is used. To this end, Dr. Miller set up his "kwashiorkor unit" apart from the hospital. At one end of it was a kitchen similar to the ones the mothers knew in their homes, with village style cookfires and pots and pans.

Dr. Miller concocted the main food himself—a mixture of corn meal and peas, both readily available. Separately, the amino acids in these two are incomplete but when mixed together they combine to form an almost complete protein. In a no-meat, no-milk community, any protein food emerges as a kind of manna.

Four meals are served daily, each always including the corn meal–peas mixture plus half an egg, manioc greens, and fruits and vegetables as available in season.

No lectures, slides, movies, or flannelgraphs are displayed. Mothers and children stay at Dr. Miller's "unit" from four to eight weeks. Typically, a recovering child increases in weight, his hemoglobin count goes up, his hair reverts to black, swelling in the stomach subsides, and his lively spirit returns. Such evidence is the best testimony to mothers of other children that Dr. Miller's diet works.

• *"Until population growth is controlled, there is little likelihood of solving other critical problems of our civilization. . . . Increased food production can be no more than palliative, and by making possible further population increase, tends to reduce the time required to pass from an acceptable standard of living to famine. . . . Man's freedom to breed at will must be curtailed." (Spoken by Frederick C. Robbins at the Association of American Medical Colleges' Institute on Medical Education and Family Planning, Washington, 1969)*

• "We have 12,000 anesthesiologists in the United States and Canada. Some countries have none and couldn't give their king proper treatment." (Spoken by Dr. Robert Hingson, who developed the "peace gun" inoculator that has saved hundreds of thousands of children abroad, at the Fourth Conference on International Health, Chicago, 1969)

• *In Nigeria a patient walked 100 miles to enter the Baptist hospital at Ogbomosho. When asked why he had not stopped at one of two hospitals on the way, he said, "This missionary hospital has a good reputation in my country."*

• "My husband came here because he loved you. He saw the great medical need and wanted to serve, both medically and spiritually.

"Why his time was so short among you we do not know. But God knows. Each of us has a time to be called home. God has called my husband Paul.

"I leave his physical body here as a memorial and a reminder to you whom he served. I know he would have chosen to stay with you." (Spoken by Lois Carlson at her husband's funeral, November 28, 1964, at Karawa, The Congo)

• *"Seeing conversions" is the outstanding spiritual satisfaction of 158 evangelical medical missionaries according to the recent survey by Medical Assistance Programs. "Seeing the gospel preached" was the second-most basic spiritual satisfaction mentioned and the missionary's spiritual growth ran a close third. (From* Medicine and Missions, *Edward R. Dayton)*

• The most frequently mentioned frustration of the missionary doctor is "inadequate language," according to a survey by Medical Assistance Programs. Second is "lack of personnel"; third, "inadequate funds"; and tied for fourth, "personal inadequacies" and "personal relationships." (From *Medicine and Missions,* Edward R. Dayton)

• *Parents were cited as the foremost influence by 158 doctors in their becoming missionaries. "Missionary speaker" ranked second and "personal contact with medical missionaries" third. "God's call to help others" and "books on missions" tied for fourth place. "Pastor" was sixth and "college teacher" seventh. (From* Medicine and Missions, *Edward R. Dayton)*

• Mysterious, remote Nepal was closed to Christian missionaries until in 1950 a Methodist missionary scientist, Dr. Robert Fleming, his doctor wife, and Presbyterian medical missionary Dr. Carl Taylor were permitted to enter and collect birds for the Chicago Museum of Natural History.

When Nepalese learned that two in the group were doctors, crowds began begging for medical treatment. Dr. Taylor operated on top of stone puja platforms dedicated to the worship of Hindu gods, on top of stone fences, and on piles of boxes and trunks. Once a mule almost knocked him down while he was trying to sew up a harelip. At one place the cold was so intense he could hardly flex his fingers.

The following year another Presbyterian doctor and his wife, Dr. and Mrs. Carl Fredericks, went to Nepal with the Flemings. Their medical services led to an invitation by Nepal's Ministry of Health to open two mission hospitals. From these beginnings have grown the United Mission to Nepal which now has five hospitals, thirteen schools and other projects in the developing country.

• *A Congolese nurse gave a typical African illustration of the value of missionary medicine to a member of the Africa Inland Mission:*

"I remember once seeing a man who didn't want to hear us preaching a gospel message. He kept his hands over his ears, blotting out the words of the speaker. Then a bee came buzzing around his head. The man had to take a hand off one ear so that he could bat the bee away. Then he heard the message. The bee made him listen.

"Our medical work is like that bee. When they come for pills and treatment for the body, they find they have to listen to the message."

• When Dr. and Mrs. David Dorr arrived at the Baptist Hospital in the disputed Gaza strip they found no baptized believers from a Muslim background in Gaza, although British missionaries had worked there for half a century. As they inquired, someone recalled, "A man was baptized once, but he was killed. There was such a riot that the British government had to send out troops and tanks."

But ten years later the Dorrs and their colleagues could be thankful for

—the Bedouin who was converted and then went into the region of Sinai to tell other Bedouins about Christ.

—the student nurses who accepted Christ and returned to hospitals in Lebanon, Kuwait, and Yemen to bear witness.

—a dentist named Suheil who emigrated to Canada, then traveled to Liberia to broadcast sermons in Arabic to the Arab world.

• *Christian missionaries returning from abroad come to a Jewish hospital in Chicago for a "parasite checkup." Mount Sinai Hospital's parasitology laboratory, directed by Dr. Russell McQuay, has tested over six thousand missionaries from more than seventy countries during the past ten years.*

Thirty-four parasites were found in the five members of a family who had been stationed in the Congo. A woman of seventy from South America had six different parasites.

One type of parasite encountered by the laboratory is referred to as having "nocturnal periodicity," because it can be seen in the blood stream between the hours of 10 p.m. and 2 a.m.

• Proof that the Muslim world welcomes agencies of Christian compassion is shown in the ministry of The Evangelical Alliance Mission's hospital in the Trucial Oman States of eastern Arabia. It was built in response to a ruling sheik's invitation to establish a mission hospital. The sheik promised "complete freedom to preach and teach the Bible"!

TEAM's Buraimi Oasis Hospital is ideally located in a lush setting dotted with tall palms. Both camels and cars meet at this crossroads of commerce for a large area of the Arabian peninsula. Thousands of Arabs have settled here, and Bedouins come into the hospital from the surrounding desert.

Recently the hospital opened an obstetrics unit. The first patient to use the new facility was Fatimah, one of the wives of Sheik Zayyid, ruler of the kingdom of Abu Dhabi on the Arabian Gulf.

• *Nurse Beth Brunemeier writes that missionaries in Nepal "commonly see evidence of blood sacrifice in Nepalese religious rituals. These people have not heard of the 'once for all' slain Lamb of God. For example, the big new motor bridge in Kathmandu will soon be completed with a human sacrifice. The body and blood of a child must be built into this bridge, to satisfy the gods who will then let the bridge stand under stress.*

"Our one prayer is that our life and work together may demonstrate to Nepal how Christ can redeem diverse peoples to one another by first redeeming us to God."

• Young Samuel Gude and his bride were on their way to medical college when their car lurched to a stop. The thin youth, who weighed only eighty pounds, climbed on the "bonnet" of the old World War II military car and began pouring gasoline into the open carburetor. Suddenly the engine backfired and a ball of flame ignited the can of gasoline in his hand. Though he flung the can away, he was still showered with the flaming fuel.

His body a burning torch, he rolled in the dust to smother the flame. "Lord, save me," he cried as bystanders threw dirt on him.

For three days he hovered between life and death; then on the fourth day when the doctor said, "You are going to live," an old Easter hymn came to him with great meaning. He lay there swathed in bandages and sang, "Death is dead, and my Lord is victor." He was able to get out of bed three months later, but the scars that remained on his hands and body would be with him a lifetime.

After receiving his M.D., Dr. Gude trained under the famous Dr. Paul Brand to do restorative surgery on leprosy patients. When this training was completed, the Nigerian government offered him six times as much salary as he would receive at a leprosy hospital in India plus three months annual vacation and paid flights back and forth from India.

But the scars reminded him of God's faithfulness and he determined that he would be faithful too. Today he is chief medical officer at the Kothar Leprosy Hospital and his skillful but scarred hands perform two hundred restorative operations each year. Forty villages surrounding the hospital have small groups of believers, and twenty groups now have chapels.

• *"We know that one drop of water cannot quench the thirst of everyone in a desert, but* it can prove there is such a thing as water. *All the world's medical need can never be completely met this side of heaven, but we can prove there is such a thing as compassion. And Christlike compassion wins men to faith in Him." (Baptist Mid-Missions Medical Department)*

• The Medical Department of Baptist Mid-Missions uses the following "Beatitudes" in seeking to arouse interest in missionary medicine:

Blessed are the poor—for then you are forced to depend on God. You use torn cloth-strips for bandages and balewa-nut oil for ointment, and God works in power to heal.

Blessed are the hungry—Patients are 100 miles from home.

They've eaten the goat they brought, and food money runs out before the day for surgery arrives. The hospital rice barrel is also low, and this month's remittance is small.

Blessed are those who weep—The tearful mother holding the limp form of her baby that malaria has just robbed of life—or the father who buries his little daughter, victim of Bilharze disease.

Blessed are the lepers—hated and driven from the village. Someday you'll be loved. Someday God will prod some healthy college student from his comfortable home to don the white coat and risk leprosy himself to help you in Christ's Name!

Blessed are you when witch doctors curse you, patients mistrust you, and even some misunderstand you and wonder why you're not doing a "spiritual work."

Be glad and leap for joy for you're better off by far than in any air-conditioned office or marble-floored hospital.

Woe to you, you who feel you have a right to luxury in a modern country with electric adjustable hospital beds, where trained nurses carry out your orders, technicians do your tests, and colleagues applaud your learned medical paper. You have your reward, and this is it, if not strictly in the will of God.

But, ah, you who languish on bamboo pallets, or straw mats, or bed springs scrounged from war surplus, you tuberculous wretches with blood-spewing cavities—you cannot have streptomycin or life-saving INH, because some say they don't want to contribute to "institutions"—just to preaching the gospel. . . . **Take heart,** for that overworked mission doctor, nurse, lab tech, assistant, will love you, and will cradle your head in his lap, and tell you of the Saviour who cares, until you take that last breath. Someday you can laugh at all disaster, comforted and singing around the throne of God.

Give and it shall be given to you—you—med student, intern, resident, nurse, lab tech—fortunate are you if God calls and you obey. You'll return from that first term, worn but thankful, tired but victorious, feeling medically out-of-date yet ready to tackle post-grad training to return to an even greater ministry for God's glory, and for eternity. Christ, the Great Physician, gave His life to redeem the world from sin. Someday, we'll wish we'd given Him more!

• *Opthalmologist Dr. Douglas Hursh considers himself only "a missionary doctor." Yet he has played the role of a missions strategist in opening missionary work in a Muslim area of north-ern Nigeria where missionaries had long been excluded or restricted.*

Desiring to help the people who have the world's highest incidence of eye diseases, he established in 1943 the Sudan Interior Mission Eye Hospital in the ancient sub-Saharan city of Kano. The hospital helped so many that it won the respect and permission of Muslim leaders for a widespread witness.

The Kano hospital is still the only institution of its kind in West Africa. Some patients arrive after walking hundreds of miles for help.

• A Southern Baptist doctor layman has received funds for his work from Pope Paul VI. After reading the book *Operation Brother's Brother,* the Pope contributed ten thousand dollars to Dr. Hingson's program of inoculating entire populations of underdeveloped countries.

Dr. Hingson, from Pittsburgh, developed a "peace gun" which teams of volunteers use to inoculate as many as half a million persons in one month. The "peace gun" injects serum under high pressure into the arm of the person receiving the inoculation under such intensity that the serum goes through clothing and skin without danger of infection or pain.

The Pope's gift will buy enough "peace gun ammunition" to save the lives of an estimated fifty thousand African babies.

• *Dr. Louis E. Carlin, Southern Baptist missionary associate in Ghana, is not a physician but a veterinarian who expresses God's love through his profession. He describes a "bush call" in the July 1969 issue of* The Commission:

"My operating room was a mud hut with a grass roof and no lights. A large audience soon assembled. In a few minutes on-lookers were watching in amazement while I administered the anesthetic, clipped and scrubbed the surgical site, and made ready for surgery.

"After putting on my rubber gloves and starting the surgery I had thirty to forty minutes of choice time to witness to this crowd. God even provided—as he almost always does—a man who knew enough English to interpret my words. The people listened quietly as I told them that I was only doing what God had allowed me to learn to do and that it was God who

performed the miracle of healing after I had opened the tissues and closed them back exactly as God had made them.

"The nanny goat was small, but God used it as an opportunity to tell people of His love."

• Today's missionary doctor can keep up with march of medicine in the homeland and continue his medical education while on furlough. The American Medical Association through its Department of Medicine and Religion offers the following services to help the overseas missionary physician meet these needs:

1. Affiliate membership in the AMA at no cost.

2. Free subscriptions to the AMA *Journal* and two specialty journals sent to the mission station where the missionary doctor serves.

3. Upon request of the missionary, the AMA Library will research medical literature and supply photocopies of pertinent articles on the subject of interest.

4. The AMA's Department of Medicine and Religion will distribute recent editions of standard medical textbooks to medical missionaries overseas in cooperation with Interchurch Medical Assistance, Inc.

5. Certain medical films for use by the missionary doctor will be made available where countries permit their use.

6. Assistance will be given the U.S. medical missionary on furlough in his continuing medical education. Effort will be made to arrange free tuition and fees while in attendance.

Acknowledgments

Many individuals and organizations helped to make this book possible. I thank J. Raymond Knighton and the staff of Medical Assistance Programs, Inc., for assistance beyond the call of duty. I thank the various missionary boards and agencies who shared material and photos from their files. I thank the American Medical Association for press hospitality during the AMA-sponsored Conference on International Health. Most of all, I thank the individual medical missionaries who allowed me to present their life stories in this volume.

My wife, Marti, collaborated with me in the editing process. Her constructive criticism and judgment enhanced by the work of the Word Books editorial staff under the direction of Floyd Thatcher gave the book a professional polish. And the "Kelly girls," Mrs. Paula and Sandi Kelly, provided expert manuscript typing.

Finally, I express appreciation to two publishers for permission to use in book form copyrighted material: The David C. Cook Publishing Company for use of "Doctor of Yemen," "Doctor of New Hope," and "Never Too Old for Service" (under the title "The Surgeon's New Career"), all © 1970; and Harvest Publications for use of "Nurse of Zambia" and "The Missionary Dentist Who Multiplied Himself," both © 1970.

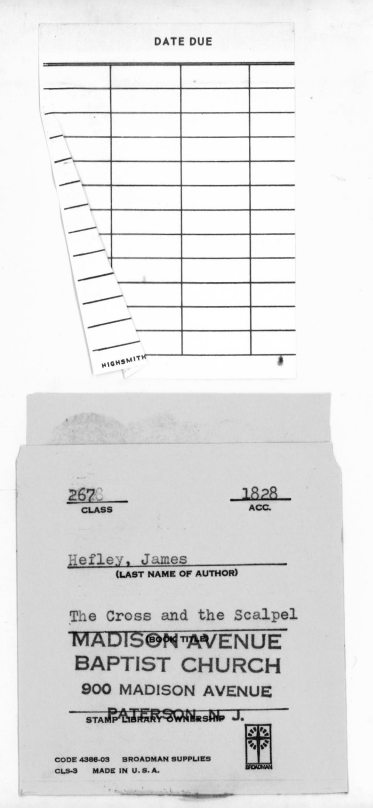